Grade 1
CONTENTS

W9-CYV-587

McGraw-Hill

My Math

Assessment Masters

Grade 1

Mc Graw Hill Education

Bothell, WA • Chicago, IL • Columbus, OH • New York, NY

connectED.mcgraw-hill.com

 **Education**

STEM McGraw-Hill is committed to providing instructional materials in Science, Technology, Engineering, and Mathematics (STEM) that give all students a solid foundation, one that prepares them for college and careers in the 21st century.

Send all inquiries to:
McGraw-Hill Education
STEM Learning Solutions Center
8787 Orion Place
Columbus, OH 43240

ISBN: 978-0-02-116178-2
MHID: 0-02-116178-X

Printed in the United States of America.

2 3 4 5 6 7 8 9 ROV 16 15 14 13 12

 *Assessment Masters*

Our mission is to provide educational resources that enable students to become the problem solvers of the 21st century and inspire them to explore careers within Science, Technology, Engineering, and Mathematics (STEM) related fields.

The *McGraw-Hill* Companies

Chapter 7 Organize and Use Graphs

Chapter 8 Measurement and Time

Chapter 9 Two-Dimensional Shapes and Equal Shares

Chapter 10 Three-Dimensional Shapes

Benchmark Tests

Teacher's Guide to Using the *Assessment Masters*

The *Assessment Masters* are organized by chapter and include assessment options to use throughout the year. In addition to the chapter assessments, you will find quarterly benchmark assessments. The answers appear at the back of the book.

All of the assessment masters are available for viewing and printing on **connectED.mcgraw-hill.com.**

Am I Ready? worksheets

- Use after the Am I Ready? pages in the Student Edition.
- Practice: On-Level students
- **AL** Review: Approaching-Level students
- **BL** Apply: Beyond-Level students

Diagnostic Test

- Tests skills needed for success in the upcoming chapter (prerequisite skills).
- Use this to retest Approaching-Level students after completing the Am I Ready? worksheet(s).

Chapter Pretest

- Assesses students' prior knowledge of the concepts in the upcoming chapter to determine pacing.
- Use before the chapter to gauge students' skill levels to determine their prior knowledge of the concepts in the chapter. You may be able to skip some topics with which all students are familiar.
- Use to determine class grouping for differentiated instruction.

Check My Progress

- Corresponds to the Check My Progress pages in the Student Edition.
- Use as a worksheet or follow-up test for Approaching-Level students who did not do well on the Student Edition Check My Progress pages.

Vocabulary Test

- Designed to be suitable for all students.
- Arranged in a variety of ways to assess the student's knowledge of the vocabulary words in the chapter.
- Can be used with Chapter Tests as an extra page of testing for the chapter.

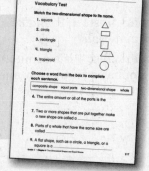

AL = Approaching Level   **BL** = Beyond Level

Chapter Tests

- **AL** Forms 1A and 1B for Approaching-Level students contain all multiple-choice questions.
- Forms 2A and 2B for On-Level students contain a mixture of multiple-choice and short-response questions.
- **BL** Forms 3A and 3B for Beyond-Level students contain all open-ended questions.
- The difference between tests A and B are the numbers used; the content assessed is the same. Test B can be used for students who are absent on the day of the test.

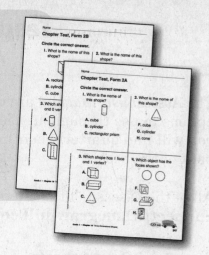

Standardized Test Practice

- Multiple-choice question format familiarizes students with experiencing standardized test format.

Oral Assessment

- Designed to be read to students and for the teacher to record students' responses. A response sheet is included for your use.
- Uses a variety of approaches including solving problems using manipulatives as well as pencil and paper.
- Can be used with all students, but may be particularly useful in assessing ELL students.

Listening Assessment

- Designed to be read to students while they record their responses.
- Includes a response sheet.

Benchmark Tests

- Includes four quarterly benchmarks in standardized test format.
- Benchmark Tests 1, 2, and 3 assess a quarter of the Student Edition materials.
- Benchmark Test 4 is a cumulative year-end test that has a heavy emphasis on the last quarter of the year.

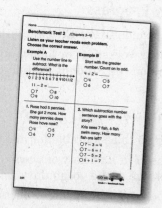

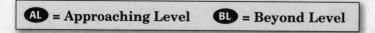

AL = Approaching Level   **BL** = Beyond Level

Name _____ Bilal _____

Am I Ready?

Practice

Write how many.

1.  _2_

2. OOOOOOOO _8_

1 2 3 4 5 6 7 8

Draw circles to show each number.

3. 3 ○ ○ ○

4. 1 ○

5. 9 ○ ○ ○ ○ ○ ○ ○ ○ ○

Use 🎲 **to show how many. Write how many there are in all.**

6.

_7_ in all

Am I Ready?

Review

The number 5 shows that there are 5 trucks.

_5_

Write how many.

1.    _7_

2.    _2_

3.    _8_

4.    _4_

5.    _1_

Grade 1 · Chapter 1 Addition Concepts

Name ___Bibal___

Am I Ready?

Apply

Use  to show how many. Write how many in all.

1. 4 brown dogs are playing. 2 white dogs come to play, too. How many dogs are playing?

___6___

2. 7 frogs are sitting on a lily pad. I more frog jumps on the lily pad. How many frogs are there altogether?

___8___

3. 6 bees sit on a flower. 3 more bees come to the flower. How many bees are there in all?

___9___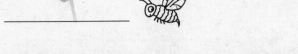

4. I bird is sitting on a branch. 3 more birds fly to the branch. How many birds are on the branch?

___4___

5. 5 turtles are on a rock. I more turtle joins them. How many turtles are there altogether?

___6___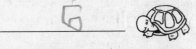

Name ___Bilal___

Diagnostic Test

Am I Ready for the Chapter?

Write how many.

1.  4

2.  7

Draw stars to show each number.

3. 6 ⚬⚬⚬⚬ ⚬⚬

4. 8 ⚬ ⚬⚬⚬⚬⚬ ⚬⚬

5. 11 ⚬⚬⚬⚬⚬⚬⚬⚬⚬⚬⚬

Solve.

6. Write how many balloons are there in all.

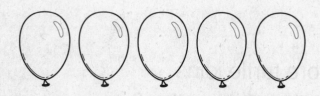 

___9___ in all

Name _Bilal_

Pretest

Write addition number sentences.

1.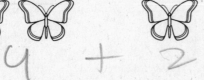

4 + 2

4 plus 2 equals __6__

4 ⊕ 2 ⊖ 6

2.

3 plus 4 equals __7__

3 ⊕ 4 = 7

3.

5 ⊕ 5 ⊖ 10

4.

6 ⊕ 3 ⊖ 9

Write the numbers. Add.

5.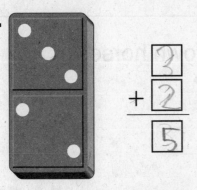

+ 3
  2
  5

6.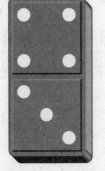

+ 4
  3
  7

Name _Bilal_

Check My Progress   *(Lessons 1 through 4)*

Add. Write the number.

Part	Part
2	**4**
Whole	
6	

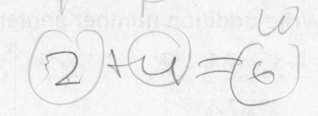

1. parts: 2 and 3; whole: ___5___

2. parts: 3 and 4; whole: ___7___

---

3. What is the sum?

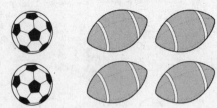

$2 + 4 =$ ___2___

4. Write the addition number sentence.

3 + 4 = 7

---

5. There are 3 white horses and 5 brown horses.
   How many horses are there in all?

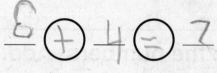

3 + 5 = 8 horses

Name __Bilal__

Check My Progress (Lessons 5 through 9)

Add. Write the numbers.

1.  $\boxed{3} + \boxed{4} = \boxed{7}$

2. $\begin{array}{r} \boxed{2} \\ + \boxed{2} \\ \hline \boxed{8} \end{array}$

3. $3 + 3 = \underline{2}$
   7

4. $2 + 5 = \underline{7}$

5. $\begin{array}{r} 4 \\ + 4 \\ \hline \boxed{8} \end{array}$

6. $\begin{array}{r} 1 \\ + 6 \\ \hline \boxed{7} \end{array}$

Write an addition number sentence to solve.

7. Jamie has 3 red beads and 5 blue beads. How many beads are there in all?

   __8__ beads

8. Walter has 2 toy cars and 3 toy trucks. How many toys does he have in all?

   __5__ toy cars

Grade 1 • Chapter 1 Addition Concepts

Copyright © The McGraw-Hill Companies, Inc. Permission is granted to reproduce for classroom use.

Name _Bilal_

Vocabulary Test

Write the correct word(s) in the blank.
Use the words from the box.

add   addition number sentence
equals (=)   plus (+)   sum

1. When you join parts together to find the sum, you

___add___.

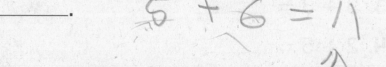

$5 + 6 = 11$

sum

2. The sign used to show having the same value is called

___Equals___.

$6 = 6$

3. The symbol used to show addition is called the

___Plus___ sign.

4. An expression using numbers and the + and = sign is

called an ___additional number sentence___.

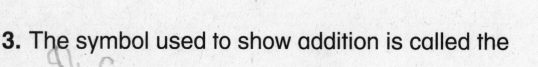

$5 + 3 = 8$

5. The answer to an addition sentence is called the

___Sum___.

$5 + 3 = 8$

Sum

Name __Bilal__

Chapter Test, Form 1A

Circle the correct answer.

1. How many apples in all?

    A. (5)

    B. 6

    C. 3

2. Which addition number sentence goes with the picture?

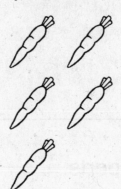 

    F. $5 + 2 = 3$

    G. $5 + 3 = 8$

    H. $5 + 2 = 7$

3. $2 + 3 = \square$

    A. 4

    B. (5)

    C. 8

4. Determine if the statement is true or false.

$1 + 6 = 6$

    F. true

    G. false

 GO on

Chapter Test, Form 1A   *(continued)*

5.   7
     $+\ 2$

    A. (9)
    B. 5
    C. 4

6.   8
     $+\ 2$

    F. 2
    G. 8
    H. (10)

7. Add the two parts.

Part	Part
5	1
Whole	
6	

    A. 2
    B. 5
    C. (6)

8. What is the sum?

$3 + 0 = \underline{3}$

    F. 0
    G. 3
    H. 5

STOP

Name _Bilal_

Chapter Test, Form 1B

Circle the correct answer.

1. How many bananas in all?

   A. 4

   B. 5

   C. 7

2. Which addition number sentence goes with this picture?

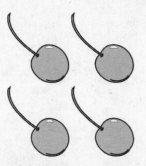 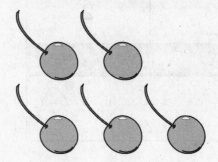

   F. $4 + 5 = 9$

   G. $5 + 4 = 10$

   H. $6 + 4 = 11$

3. $3 + 2 = \boxed{5}$

   A. 6

   B. 3

   C. 5

4. $7 + 1 = \boxed{6}$

   F. 9

   G. 8

   H. 10

Chapter Test, Form 1B *(continued)*

5. $4 + 3 = \boxed{7}$

    A. 11

    B. 9

    C. 7 ⟵ *(circled)*

6. Determine if the statement is true or false.

$6 + 4 = 10$

    F. true *(circled)*

    G. false

7. Add the two parts.

Part	Part
3	2
Whole	
5	

    A. 7

    B. 4

    C. 5 *(circled)*

8. What is the sum?

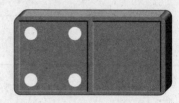

$4 + 0 = \underline{4}$

    F. 4 *(circled)*

    G. 6

    H. 3

Name _____

Chapter Test, Form 2A

Circle the correct answer.

1. How many peppers in all?

  A. 3
  B. 5
  C. 7
  D. 8

2. Which addition number sentence matches the picture?

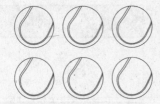

  F. $2 + 7 = 9$
  G. $2 + 6 = 8$
  H. $0 + 6 = 6$
  I. $4 + 8 = 12$

3. $3 + 1 = \boxed{4}$

  A. 4
  B. 5
  C. 6
  D. 7

4. $3 + 5 = \boxed{8}$

  F. 5
  G. 6
  H. 7
  I. 8

5. $5 + 4 = \boxed{9}$

  A. 8
  B. 9
  C. 10
  D. 11

6. Determine if the statement is true or false.

$7 + 3 = 9$

  F. true
  G. false

GO on

Chapter Test, Form 2A   (continued)

Read each question carefully. Write your answer on the line provided.

7. Find the sum of the parts. Write the whole.

Part	Part
6	2
Whole	
8	

8. What is the sum?

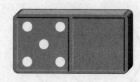

$5 + 0 = $ 5

9. Edward has 2 pairs of black shoes and 1 pair of brown shoes. How many pairs of shoes does he have in all? Write an addition number sentence.

2 + 1 = 3

10. Write the addition number sentence that matches the picture.

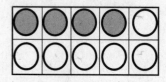

4 + 6 = 4

Grade 1 · Chapter 1 Addition Concepts

Name _____ 8ilal

Circle the correct answer.

1. How many flowers in all?

   A. 5
   B. 8
   C. 7
   D. 10

2. Which addition number sentence matches the picture?

   F. $4 + 5 = 9$
   G. $3 + 6 = 9$
   H. $4 + 0 = 4$
   I. $6 + 7 = 13$

3. $4 + 2 = \boxed{6}$

   A. 4
   B. 5
   C. 6
   D. 7

4. $5 + 4 = \boxed{9}$

   F. 8
   G. 9
   H. 10
   I. 11

5.
$$\begin{array}{r} 2 \\ + 5 \\ \hline 7 \end{array}$$

   A. 7
   B. 8
   C. 10
   D. 11

6. Determine if the statement is true or false.

$3 + 5 = 7$

   F. true
   G. false

GO on

Chapter Test, Form 2B *(continued)*

Read each question carefully. Write your answer on the line provided.

7. Find the sum of the two parts. Write the whole.

Part	Part
5	2
Whole	
7	

8. What is the sum?

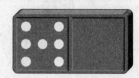

$7 + 0 = \underline{7}$

9. Lin has 3 red shirts and 4 green shirts. How many shirts does Lin have? Write an addition number sentence.

$\underline{4} + \underline{3} = \underline{7}$

10. Write the addition number sentence that matches the picture.

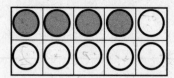

$\underline{4} + \underline{6} = \underline{10}$

STOP

Name _Bilal_

Chapter Test, Form 3A

Write the correct answer.

1. How many ladybugs in all?

_4_

2. Write the addition number sentence that matches the picture.

_4 + 3 = 7_

3. $4 + 1 = \boxed{5}$

4. $0 + 6 = \boxed{6}$

5. $6 + 2 = \boxed{8}$

6. Determine if the statement is true or false.

$2 + 6 = 8$

(true)   false

GO on

7. Find the sum of the two parts. Write the whole.

Part	Part
5	4
Whole	
_____	

8. 3 penguins are on the ice. 2 more penguins run to join them. How many penguins altogether? Write the correct addition number sentence.

_____ + _____ = _____

9. Write the addition number sentence that matches the counters.

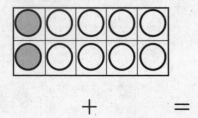

_____ + _____ = _____

10. What is the sum?

6 + 0 = _____

11. Akio sees 7 ants. He sees 3 more ants coming. How many ants are there now?
Write the addition number sentence across and down to solve.

☐ + ☐ = ☐

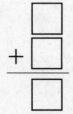

Name _____

Chapter Test, Form 3B

Write the correct answer.

1. How many snails in all?

_____

2. Write the addition number sentence that goes with the picture.

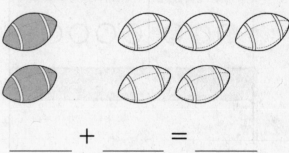

_____ + _____ = _____

3. $3 + 3 = \boxed{}$

4. $9 + 0 = \boxed{}$

5. $2 + 5 = \boxed{}$

6. Determine if the statement is true or false.

$8 + 2 = 11$

true   false

GO on

Chapter Test, Form 3B *(continued)*

7. Add the two parts. Write the whole.

Part	Part
●●●	○○○○○
Whole	
_____	

8. 6 cows are eating. 3 more cows join them. How many cows are eating now? Write the addition number sentence.

_____ + _____ = _____

9. Write the addition number sentence that goes with the counters.

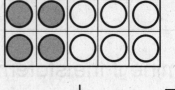

_____ + _____ = _____

10. What is the sum?

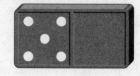

5 + 0 = _____

11. Jill had 3 fish. She gets 4 more. How many fish does Jill have now? Write the addition number sentence across and down to solve.

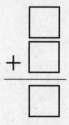

Grade 1 · Chapter 1 Addition Concepts

Name _____

Standardized Test Practice

**Listen as your teacher reads each problem.
Choose the correct answer.**

Example A

How many turtles are there in all?

   ○ 4   ○ 8
   ○ 5   ○ 9

Example B

How many umbrellas are there in all?

   ○ 5   ○ 7
   ○ 6   ○ 8

1. How many hearts are there in all?

   ○ 3   ○ 6
   ○ 5   ○ 7

2. Which addition number sentence goes with this picture?

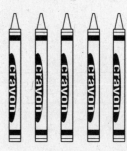

○ $5 + 3 = 8$
○ $6 + 4 = 10$
○ $5 + 4 = 9$
○ $6 + 5 = 11$

GO on

Standardized Test Practice (continued)

**Listen as your teacher reads each problem.
Choose the correct answer.**

3. $3 + 3 =$ _____

   ○ 6
   ○ 3
   ○ 5
   ○ 7

4. $8 + 1 =$ _____

   ○ 1
   ○ 8
   ○ 9
   ○ 10

5. $3 + 2 =$ _____

   ○ 4
   ○ 5
   ○ 6
   ○ 7

6. $4 + 1 =$ _____

   ○ 7
   ○ 6
   ○ 5
   ○ 4

Oral Assessment

Preparation: Counters and connecting cubes are needed for this assessment.

Directions: This test targets those students who have developing verbal skills—both oral and written. Ask the questions below and have students record their answers, or record the answers they supply.

1. Tell students this story problem: 3 puppies bark. 4 more puppies bark. Ask: *How many counters can you use to show how many puppies barked?*

2. Have students add 1 cube and 4 cubes to find the whole.

3. Tell students this story problem: There are 2 students reading. 4 more students join them. Ask: *How many students are reading in all?* Have students write the addition number sentence and solve.

4. Have students write the addition number sentence for 3 plus 6 equals 9.

5. Ask: *What is 8 + 0?*

6. Ask: *What is 4 + 2?*

7. Ask: *What is 2 + 5?*

8. Ask: *What is 6 + 4?*

9. Tell students this story problem: A bird laid 3 eggs. Another bird laid 5 more. Ask: *How many eggs did the birds lay in all?* Have students draw a picture and solve.

Notes

_____

_____

_____

_____

_____

Name _____

 Oral Assessment Response Sheet

1. _____   2. _____

3. _____   4. _____

5. _____   6. _____

7. _____   8. _____

9. _____
   _____

Name _____

 # Listening Assessment

Directions: Ask students to complete each of the following tasks.

1. Show 5 counters. Show 3 more. How many counters in all?

2. Draw 3 stars. Draw 4 more stars. Write an addition sentence. How many stars in all?

3. Start with the number 6. Add 0. What is the answer?

4. Heidi has 4 paintbrushes. She buys 1 more. Write the addition number sentence. How many does she have in all?

5. Draw 5 counters and color. Draw 5 more counters. Write the addition number sentence.

6. Juan ate 2 peas. He ate 2 more. Draw a picture to show the number of peas Juan ate. Write an addition number sentence to show how many peas Juan ate in all.

Notes

_____

_____

_____

_____

Name _____

 Listening Assessment Response Sheet

I. _____

2. _____

_____ ◯ _____ ◯ _____

3. _____

4. _____ ◯ _____ ◯ _____

5.

_____ ◯ _____ ◯ _____

6. _____

_____ ◯ _____ ◯ _____

Am I Ready?

Practice

Write how many.

1.  _____

2.  _____

Draw dots to show how many.

3. 7

4. 3

5. Put an X on 2 ducks. Write how many are left.

 _____

6. Put an X on 4 bugs. Write how many are left.

 _____

Name _____

Am I Ready?

Review

You started with 5 strawberries.
Put an X on 3 strawberries.
There are 2 strawberries left.

Put an X on 2 pieces of fruit. Write how many are left.

1.

   _____

2.

   _____

3.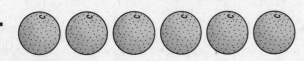

   _____

4.

   _____

5.

   _____

Am I Ready?

Apply

Use ◯ to solve. Write the answers.

1. There are 6 ducks in a pond. 2 fly away.
   How many ducks stayed in the pond?

   _____ ducks

2. Jack had 9 toy cars. He gave 7 away. How
   many cars does Jack have now?

   _____ cars

3. There are 10 clouds in the sky. 3 clouds
   go away. How many clouds are left?

   _____ clouds

4. Sara had 12 grapes. She ate 6 of them.
   How many grapes does Sara have now?

   _____ grapes

5. 11 leaves are on a tree. 9 fall off. How many
   leaves are left on the tree?

   _____ leaves

Diagnostic Test

Am I Ready for the Chapter?

Write how many.

1.

_____

2.

_____

Draw dots to show how many.

3. 5

4. 9

5. 6

Put an X on 3 fish. Write how many are left.

6.

_____

Name _____

Pretest

Write the subtraction number sentence.

1.

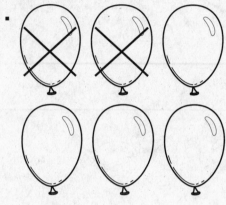

___ ◯ ___ ◯ ___

2.

___ ◯ ___ ◯ ___

Solve.

3. 5 apples grew on a tree. 2 fell off. How many apples are left? _____

4. $9 - 4 =$ _____

5. $7 - 0 =$ _____

6. $10 - 4 =$ _____

7. $3 - 3 =$ _____

Name _____

Check My Progress   (Lessons 1 through 5)

Write the subtraction number sentence.

1.

_____ ◯− _____ ◯= _____

2.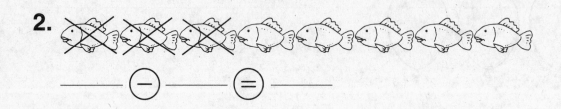

_____ ◯− _____ ◯= _____

3. There are 9 frogs on a log. 4 frogs jump off
   the log. How many frogs are left on the log?

_____ frogs

4. There are 7 birds sitting in the tree. 7 of the birds
   fly away. How many birds are left in the tree?

_____ birds

Subtract.

5. 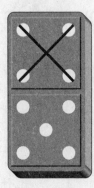 $\begin{array}{r} 9 \\ -4 \\ \hline \square \end{array}$

6. 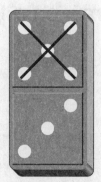 $\begin{array}{r} 8 \\ -5 \\ \hline \square \end{array}$

Check My Progress *(Lessons 6 through 9)*

Write the subtraction number sentence.

1.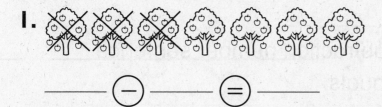

————— ⊖ ————— ⊜ —————

Subtract.

2. 6 − 3 = _____

3. 5 − 5 = _____

4. 8
   −4
   ☐

5. 7
   −2
   ☐

Write the subtraction number sentence.

6. 6 birds are blue. 2 birds are red. How many less birds are red than blue?

_____ − _____ = _____ birds

7. 8 apples are green. 3 apples are red. How many more apples are green than red?

_____ − _____ = _____ apples

Vocabulary Test

Circle the correct answer.

1. 9 − 7 = 2 is a _____.
   A. sum   C. subtraction number sentence
   B. difference   D. equals

2. When you take away, you _____.
   F. add   H. difference
   G. subtract   I. plus

3. 7 − 4 = 3
   In this problem, the 3 is called the _____.
   A. difference   C. minus
   B. sum   D. subtraction number sentence

4. 2 + 4 = 6 and 6 − 4 = 2 are called _____
   because they use the same numbers.
   F. sum   H. subtraction number sentence
   G. difference   I. related facts

5. The sign used to show subtraction is called
   the _____ sign.
   A. difference   C. minus (−)
   B. sum   D. plus (+)

Name _____

Chapter Test, Form 1A

Read each question. Circle the correct answer.

1. Ann has 6 buckets. 5 have sand in them. How many buckets are empty?

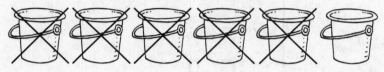

A. 1   **B.** 6   **C.** 7

2. There are 4 tigers. There is 1 lion. How many fewer lions are there than tigers?

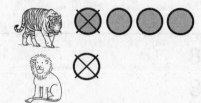

  F. $3 - 2 = 1$ fewer lion

  G. $4 - 1 = 3$ fewer lions

  H. $4 - 2 = 2$ fewer lions

3. Look at the addition number sentence below. Which of the following shows a related subtraction fact?

$1 + 7 = 8$

  A. $8 - 7 = 1$ **B.** $7 - 1 = 6$ **C.** $8 + 1 = 9$

4. What is the difference?

Part	Part
4	
Whole	
6	

  F. 10

  G. 3

  H. 2

GO on

Chapter Test, Form 1A   (continued)

Circle the the correct answer.

5. $10 - 0 =$

   A. 1

   B. 9

   C. 10

6. $4 - 3 =$

   F. 1

   G. 0

   H. 2

7. $\begin{array}{r} 8 \\ -\ 8 \\ \hline \end{array}$

   A. 0

   B. 7

   C. 1

8. $\begin{array}{r} 9 \\ -\ 4 \\ \hline \end{array}$

   F. 6

   G. 4

   H. 5

9. Which subtraction number sentence goes with the picture?

   A. $5 - 0 = 5$

   B. $5 - 2 = 3$

   C. $3 - 2 = 1$

10. Which subtraction number sentence goes with the picture?

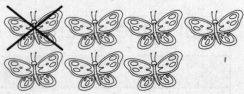

   F. $7 - 1 = 6$

   G. $6 - 1 = 5$

   H. $6 + 1 = 7$

Name _____

Chapter Test, Form 1B

Read each question. Circle the correct answer.

1. Leo buys 4 buttons. 1 button has stripes. How many buttons do not have stripes?

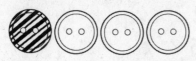

   A. 1   **B.** 2   **C.** 3

2. There are 6 snakes. There are 2 frogs. How many fewer frogs are there than snakes?

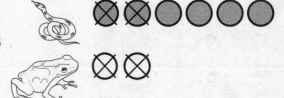

   F. $4 - 4 = 0$ fewer frogs

   G. $6 - 2 = 4$ fewer frogs

   H. $6 - 3 = 3$ fewer frogs

3. Look at the addition number sentence below. Which of the following shows a related subtraction fact?

   $4 + 3 = 7$

   A. $7 - 1 = 6$ **B.** $4 - 3 = 1$ **C.** $7 - 3 = 4$

4. What is the difference?

Part	Part
1	
Whole	
2	

   F. 1

   G. 2

   H. 3

Chapter Test, Form 1B (continued)

Circle the correct answer.

5. $9 - 1 =$

    A. 9

    B. 8

    C. 0

6. $6 - 0 =$

    F. 2

    G. 5

    H. 6

7.   9
    $- 8$

    A. 7

    B. 2

    C. 1

8.   5
    $- 5$

    F. 10

    G. 5

    H. 0

9. Which subtraction number sentence goes with the picture?

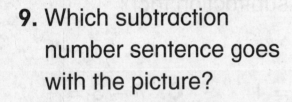

    A. $5 - 5 = 5$

    B. $5 - 4 = 1$

    C. $5 + 4 = 9$

10. Which subtraction number sentence goes with the picture?

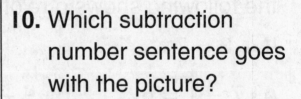
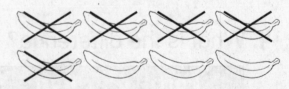

    F. $5 - 3 = 2$

    G. $8 - 0 = 8$

    H. $8 - 5 = 3$

Name _____

Chapter Test, Form 2A

Circle the correct answer.

1. There are 5 birds. 1 flies away. How many birds are left?

A. 7
B. 6
C. 5
D. 4

2. There are 6 flowers. There are 4 bees. How many more flowers are there than bees?

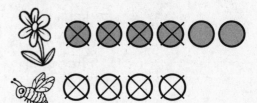

F. 4 − 3 = 1 more flower
G. 8 − 7 = 1 more flower
H. 6 − 4 = 2 more flowers
I. 10 − 6 = 4 more flowers

3. Look at the addition number sentence below. Which of the following show a related subtraction fact?

5 + 3 = 8
A. 8 − 1 = 7
B. 5 − 3 = 2
C. 8 − 4 = 4
D. 8 − 3 = 5

4. What is the difference?

Part	Part
1	
Whole	
8	

F. 1
G. 3
H. 7
I. 9

GO on

Chapter Test, Form 2A *(continued)*

Read each question. Write the answer.

7. $\begin{array}{r} 7 \\ -\ 5 \\ \hline \end{array}$

8. $\begin{array}{r} 9 \\ -\ 9 \\ \hline \end{array}$

---

9. Write the subtraction number sentence that goes with the picture.

———$\bigcirc$———$\bigcirc$———

10. Write the subtraction number sentence that goes with the picture.

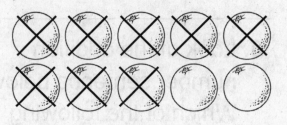

———$\bigcirc$———$\bigcirc$———

STOP

Chapter Test, Form 2B

Read each question. Circle the correct answer.

1. There are 6 cats.
1 runs away.
How many are left?

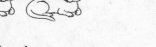

A. 1   **B.** 5

C. 6   **D.** 7

2. There are 7 flowers.
There are 2 bees. How
many more flowers are
there than bees?

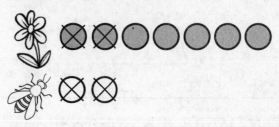

F. $5 + 2 = 7$ more flowers

G. $2 + 5 = 7$ more flowers

H. $7 - 5 = 2$ more flowers

I. $7 - 2 = 5$ more flowers

3. Look at the following
addition number sentence
below. Which of the
following shows a related
subtraction fact?

$4 + 5 = 9$

A. $9 + 4 = 13$

B. $9 - 5 = 4$

C. $5 - 4 = 1$

D. $9 - 6 = 3$

4. What is the difference?

Part	Part
2	
Whole	
5	

F. 0

G. 1

H. 2

I. 3

Chapter Test, Form 2B *(continued)*

Read each question. Write the answer.

5.
```
   8
 - 4
 ___
```

6.
```
   5
 - 5
 ___
```

---

7. Write the subtraction number sentence that goes with the picture.

○ — ○ —

8. Write the subtraction number sentence that goes with the picture.

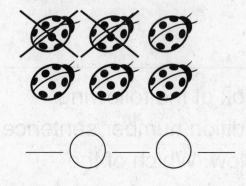

— ○ — ○ —

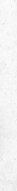

STOP

Grade 1 • Chapter 2 Subtraction Concepts

Name _____

Chapter Test, Form 3A

Read each question. Write the correct answer.

1. There are 5 butterflies.
3 fly away.
How many butterflies
are left?

_____ butterflies

2. There are 7 marbles.
There is one beach ball.
How many fewer beach
balls are there than
marbles?

_____ fewer beach balls

3. Look at the addition
number sentence below.
Write a related subtraction
number sentence.

$1 + 7 = 8$

_____ – _____ = _____

or

_____ – _____ = _____

4. What is the difference?

Part	Part
4	
Whole	
6	

$6 - 4 =$ _____

5. Write a subtraction number sentence to match the picture.

_____ ◯ _____ ◯ _____

6. $5 - 4 =$ _____

7. $7 - 3 =$ _____

8. $\begin{array}{r} 9 \\ -\ 6 \\ \hline \end{array}$

9. Write the subtraction number sentence.

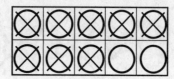

____ ◯ ____ ◯ ____

10. Georgia made 10 bracelets. She gave 8 of them away. How many bracelets does she have left?

_____ bracelets

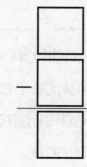

11. $9 - 6 =$ _____

12. $\begin{array}{r} 7 \\ -\ 3 \\ \hline \end{array}$

Name _____

Chapter Test, Form 3B

Read each question. Write the correct answer.

1. There are 4 birds.
1 flies away.
How many are there
now?

_____ birds

2. There are 8 hot dogs.
There are 4 hamburgers.
How many fewer
hamburgers are there
than hot dogs?

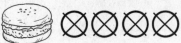

_____ fewer hamburgers

3. Look at the addition
number sentence below.
Write a related subtraction
number sentence.

$5 + 2 = 7$

_____ – _____ = _____

or

_____ – _____ = _____

4. What is the difference?

Part	Part
0	
Whole	
8	

$8 - 0 = $ _____

5. Write the subtraction sentence to match the picture.

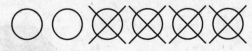

_____ ◯ _____ ◯ _____

Name _____

Chapter Test, Form 3B   *(continued)*

6. 9 − 1 = _____

7.   8
       − 4
       _____

8.   9
       − 5
       _____

9. Write the subtraction sentence.

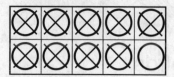

_____ ◯ _____ ◯ _____

10. John played catch with his dad. His dad threw the ball 10 times. John caught it 8 times. How many times did John miss a catch?

_____ ◯ _____ ◯ _____

11.   6
        − 3
        _____

12. 10 − 4 = _____

STOP

Name _____

Standardized Test Practice

Listen as your teacher reads each problem. Choose the correct answer.

Example A

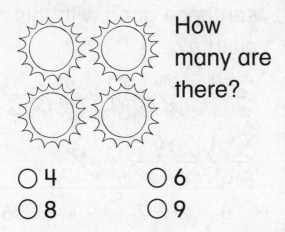

How many are there?

○ 4   ○ 6
○ 8   ○ 9

Example B

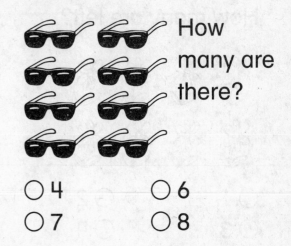

How many are there?

○ 4   ○ 6
○ 7   ○ 8

---

1. How many birds in all?

○ 3   ○ 5
○ 6   ○ 8

2. Put an X on 3 bugs. How many are left?

○ 4   ○ 5
○ 3   ○ 7

GO on

Standardized Test Practice *(continued)*

Listen as your teacher reads each problem.
Choose the correct answer.

3. Put an X on 4 flowers. How many are left?

○ 1   ○ 2
○ 3   ○ 4

4. Which subtraction sentence goes with this picture?

○ 8 − 2 = 7   ○ 9 − 3 = 6
○ 9 − 4 = 5   ○ 10 − 5 = 5

5.

```
    7
  − 0
  ____
```

○ 7   ○ 6
○ 5   ○ 4

6. Julia had 7 shirts. She gave 3 away. How many shirts does she have left?

○ 5   ○ 4
○ 3   ○ 2

7.

```
    5
  − 4
  ____
```

○ 3   ○ 2
○ 1   ○ 0

8. Miles found 3 rocks. He gave 1 to his brother. How many rocks does he have left?

○ 5   ○ 4
○ 3   ○ 2

Name _____

 # Oral Assessment

Preparation: A set of connecting cubes and board access are needed for this assessment.

Directions: This test targets those students who have developing verbal skills—both oral and written. Ask the questions below and have students record their answers, or record the answers they supply.

1. Read this number story: *6 birds were outside the window. 2 flew away*. Ask: *How many birds are still outside the window?*

2. Show 8 connecting cubes. Then take 5 of the cubes away. Ask: *How many cubes are left?*

3. On the board, draw 7 circles. Cross out 4 circles. Ask: *How many circles did I draw?* Ask: *How many circles did I put an X on? How many circles don't have an X?*
   Have the student write the subtraction sentence.

4. On the board, draw 9 squares. Then cross out all of the squares. Ask: *What is 9 minus 9?*

5. Have the students draw a picture to solve 6 − 5.

6. Ask: *What is 9 − 4?*

7. Ask: *What is 8 − 6?*

Notes

_____

_____

_____

_____

_____

Oral Assessment Response Sheet

1. _____   2. _____

3. _____, _____, _____   4. _____

———◯———◯———

5. _____

6. _____   7. _____

Name _____

 # Listening Assessment

Directions: Ask students to complete each of the following tasks.

1. Draw a group of eight circles. Write how many circles you drew. Color two circles. Write the number of circles that are not colored.

2. Draw seven stars. Color five stars yellow. Write the number of stars that are not yellow.

3. Draw nine squares. Draw Xs on three squares. Write the subtraction sentence.

4. Draw a picture to show 6 − 1. Write a subtraction sentence to show the difference.

5. Draw a picture to show 9 − 4. Write a subtraction sentence to show the difference.

6. Draw a picture to show 8 − 7. Write a subtraction sentence to show the difference.

7. Draw a domino with 5 dots on one side and 4 dots on the other side. Cross out 4 dots. Write a subtraction number sentence across and down.

Notes

_____

_____

_____

_____

Name _____

 Listening Assessment Response Sheet

1.

_____   _____

2.

_____

3.

___ ◯ ___ ◯ ___

4.

___ ◯ ___ ◯ ___

5.

___ ◯ ___ ◯ ___

6.

___ ◯ ___ ◯ ___

7.

___ ◯ ___ ◯ ___

Name _____

Am I Ready?

Practice

Add.

1. 5 + 1 = _____

2. 6 + 4 = _____

3. 5 + 3 = _____

4. 9 + 1 = _____

5. 2 + 7 = _____

6. 4 + 4 = _____

7. 5 + 0 = _____

8. 9 + 3 = _____

9. 3 + 3 = _____

Use the pictures to write an addition number sentence.

10.

_____ ◯ _____ ◯ _____

Name ______________________________

Am I Ready?

Review

> **Addition sentences can be written across or up and down.**
>
> ○○ ●●●
>
> 2 + 3 = 5
>
> $$\begin{array}{r} 2 \\ +\ 3 \\ \hline 5 \end{array}$$ ○○ ●●●

Add.

1. 4 + 2 = ______

2. 5 + 3 = ______

3. 7 + 2 = ______

4. 3 + 1 = ______

5. $\begin{array}{r} 2 \\ +\ 1 \\ \hline \end{array}$

6. $\begin{array}{r} 6 \\ +\ 4 \\ \hline \end{array}$

7. $\begin{array}{r} 5 \\ +\ 5 \\ \hline \end{array}$

8. $\begin{array}{r} 9 \\ +\ 2 \\ \hline \end{array}$

9. $\begin{array}{r} 4 \\ +\ 5 \\ \hline \end{array}$

10. $\begin{array}{r} 8 \\ +\ 3 \\ \hline \end{array}$

Am I Ready?

Apply

Solve.

1. Ben gave 4 nuts to a squirrel. Ben gave
   2 nuts to a chipmunk. How many nuts did
   Ben give away? _____ nuts

2. There are 5 spoons in the drawer. There are
   4 spoons on the table. How many spoons
   are there in all? _____ spoons

3. Maya gave 3 flowers to her aunt. She gave
   3 flowers to her uncle. How many flowers
   did Maya give away? _____ flowers

4. Ray has 6 baseball cards. Luis has
   5 baseball cards. If they put all of their
   cards together, how many cards will Ray
   and Luis have? _____ cards

5. There are 4 lemons on the tree. There are
   6 lemons on the ground. How many lemons
   are there in all? _____ lemons

Diagnostic Test

Am I Ready for the Chapter?

1. Circle the addition sign.

+   −   =

2. Circle the equal sign.

+   −   =

Add.

3. 4
  +4
  ____

4. 1
  +5
  ____

5. 6
  +4
  ____

6. 3
  +2
  ____

7. 1
  +4
  ____

8. 4
  +2
  ____

9. 5
  +3
  ____

10. 0
  +3
  ____

11. 5
  +5
  ____

Use the picture to write an addition number sentence.

12.

___ ◯ ___ ◯ ___

Grade 1 • Chapter 3 Addition Strategies to 20

Name _____

Pretest

Use the number line to help you add. Write the sum.

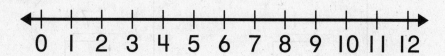

0 1 2 3 4 5 6 7 8 9 10 11 12

I. $5 + 2 =$ _____

2. $7 + 5 =$ _____

Write the sum.

3. 3
     $+ 3$

4. 3
     $+ 4$

5. Count on to add.

$6 + 2 =$ _____

6. Make a ten. Write that number. Add the other number to find the sum.

$⑥ + ④ + 3 =$ _____

7. Write the addends. Add.

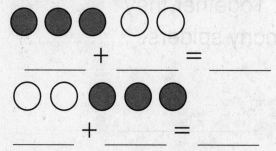

_____ + _____ = _____

_____ + _____ = _____

Check My Progress *(Lessons 1 through 5)*

Circle the greater number. Count on to add.

1.   6
     + 2
     ☐

2.   5
     + 1
     ☐

3.   1
     + 7
     ☐

Use the number line to add.

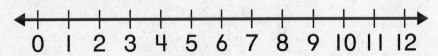

0 1 2 3 4 5 6 7 8 9 10 11 12

4.   7
     + 4

5.   6
     + 3

6.   2
     + 5

Write the sum. Circle the doubles facts.

7. 3 + 5 = _____

8. 8 + 8 = _____

9. 6 + 7 = _____

10. 9 + 9 = _____

11. Trinity and Gordon counted spiders.
Gordon counted 6 spiders. Together they
counted 11 spiders. How many spiders
did Trinity count?

_____ spiders

Grade 1 • Chapter 3 Addition Strategies to 20

Vocabulary Test

Use the words in the box. Write your answers.

addends	count on	doubles
doubles minus 1	doubles plus 1	number line

1. A line with number labels is called a

_____.

2. To add on a number line, start with the greater

number and _____.

3. Any numbers or quantities being added together

are called _____.

4. When you add with doubles and add one more,

it is called _____.

5. Two addends that are the same are

_____.

6. When you add with doubles and subtract one,

it is called _____.

Name _____

Chapter Test, Form 1A

Circle the correct answer.

1. Count on to add.

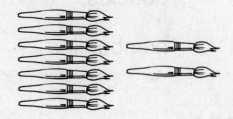

$7 + 2 = $ _____

A. 9   **B.** 10   **C.** 11

2. Circle the greater number. Count on to add.

$4 + 2 = $ _____

F. 2
G. 6
H. 7

Use the number line to add. What is the sum?

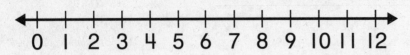

3. $8 + 4 = $ _____

A. 12   **B.** 13   **C.** 14

4. $9 + 3 = $ _____

F. 10   **G.** 11   **H.** 12

---

5. Which number sentence matches the picture?

A. $4 + 4 = 8$

B. $3 + 3 = 6$

C. $2 + 2 = 4$

6. Find the sum.

$$\begin{array}{r} 7 \\ + 8 \\ \hline \end{array}$$

F. 13

G. 14

H. 15

GO on

Chapter Test, Form IA (continued)

Circle the correct answer.

7. Which doubles fact will help you find the sum of 1 + 2?

   A. 0 + 0 = 0

   B. 1 + 1 = 2

   C. 3 + 3 = 6

8. Make a ten to add. Which number is missing?

$$\begin{array}{r} 8 \\ +\ 7 \\ \hline 15 \end{array} \longrightarrow \begin{array}{r} 10 \\ +\ \boxed{} \\ \hline 15 \end{array}$$

   F. 4   **G.** 5   **H.** 6

9. Which addends match the picture?

   _____ + _____ = 8   _____ + _____ = 8

   A. 5 + 2; 2 + 5   **B.** 5 + 4; 4 + 5   **C.** 5 + 3; 3 + 5

10. Casey has 3 cans of food for the food drive. Jen has 2 cans of food. Pat has 3 cans of food. How many cans do they have in all?

   F. 6

   G. 8

   H. 9

Chapter Test, Form IB

Circle the correct answer.

1. Count on to add.

6 + 2 = _____

A. 9   **B.** 8   **C.** 7

2. Circle the greater number. Count on to add.

5 + 3 = _____

F. 8   **G.** 6   **H.** 5

Use the number line to add. What is the sum?

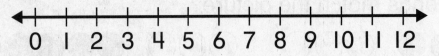

3. 6 + 4 = _____

A. 9   **B.** 10   **C.** 11

4. 8 + 2 = _____

F. 12   **G.** 11   **H.** 10

---

5. Which number sentence matches the picture?

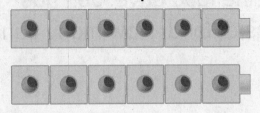

A. 6 + 6 = 12
B. 5 + 5 = 10
C. 4 + 4 = 8

6. Find the sum.

$$\begin{array}{r} 6 \\ + 7 \\ \hline \square \end{array}$$

F. 12
G. 13
H. 14

GO on

Name _____

Chapter Test, Form 1B *(continued)*

Circle the correct answer.

7. Which doubles fact will help you find the sum of 2 + 3?

A. 1 + 1 = 2

B. 2 + 2 = 4

C. 4 + 4 = 8

8. Make a ten to add. Which number is missing?

$$\begin{array}{r} 7 \\ + \ 4 \\ \hline \boxed{11} \end{array} \longrightarrow \begin{array}{r} 10 \\ + \ \boxed{} \\ \hline 11 \end{array}$$

F. 1 **G.** 2 **H.** 3

9. Which addends match the picture?

⬤⬤⬤⬤ ○○○   ○○○ ⬤⬤⬤⬤

_____ + _____ = 7   _____ + _____ = 7

A. 5 + 3; 3 + 5 **B.** 4 + 3; 3 + 4 **C.** 3 + 2; 2 + 3

10. The van has 4 cup holders in the front seat, 4 cup holders in the middle seat, and 3 cup holders in the back seat. How many cup holders in all?

F. 10

G. 11

H. 12

STOP

Name _____

Chapter Test, Form 2A

Circle the correct answer.

1. Count on to add.

9 + 3 = _____

A. 9   **B.** 10

C. 11   **D.** 12

2. Circle the greater number. Count on to add.

6 + 2 = _____

F. 5   **G.** 6

H. 7   **I.** 8

Use the number line to add. What is the sum?

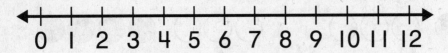

0 1 2 3 4 5 6 7 8 9 10 11 12

3. 7 + 2 = _____

A. 9   **B.** 10

C. 11   **D.** 12

4. 6 + 5 = _____

F. 8   **G.** 9

H. 10   **I.** 11

Find the sum.

5. 7 + 7 = _____

A. 15   **B.** 14

C. 13   **D.** 12

6.   7
      + 8
      ____

F. 15   **G.** 14

H. 13   **I.** 12

GO on

Chapter Test, Form 2A *(continued)*

Write the correct answer.

7. Write a doubles fact that will help you find the sum of 6 + 7.

_____ + _____ = _____

8. On Monday there were 3 students absent in Miss Cook's class. On Tuesday there were 5 students absent and on Wednesday 4 students were absent. How many students were absent in all?

_____ students

9. Make a ten to add. Write the missing numbers.

$$\begin{array}{r} 8 \\ +\ 5 \\ \hline \ \square \end{array} \longrightarrow \begin{array}{r} 10 \\ +\ \square \\ \hline \square \end{array}$$

10. Make a ten. Write that number. Add the other number to find the sum.

②+⑧+ 1 = _____

□

STOP

Name _____

Chapter Test, Form 2B

Circle the correct answer.

1. Count on to add.

$5 + 2 =$ _____

A. 6   **B.** 7

C. 8   **D.** 9

2. Circle the greater number. Count on to add.

$5 + 3 =$ _____

F. 5   **G.** 6

H. 7   **I.** 8

Use the number line to add. What is the sum?

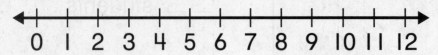

$$0 \quad 1 \quad 2 \quad 3 \quad 4 \quad 5 \quad 6 \quad 7 \quad 8 \quad 9 \quad 10 \quad 11 \quad 12$$

3. $6 + 3 =$ _____

A. 9   **B.** 8

C. 7   **D.** 6

4. $9 + 2 =$ _____

F. 9   **G.** 10

H. 11   **I.** 12

Find the sum.

5. $5 + 5 =$ _____

A. 12   **B.** 11

C. 10   **D.** 9

6.
$$\begin{array}{r} 5 \\ +6 \\ \hline \end{array}$$

F. 10   **G.** 11

H. 12   **I.** 13

GO on

Chapter Test, Form 2B *(continued)*

Write the correct answer.

7. Write a doubles fact that will help you find the sum of $8 + 9$.

_____ + _____ = _____

8. Jason ate 7 carrot sticks for lunch on Tuesday. He ate 5 sticks on Wednesday. He ate 4 sticks on Thursday. How many carrot sticks did he eat in all?

_____ carrot sticks

9. Make a ten to add. Write the missing numbers.

$$\begin{array}{c} 8 \\ +\ 4 \\ \hline \boxed{} \end{array} \longrightarrow \begin{array}{c} 10 \\ +\ \boxed{} \\ \hline \boxed{} \end{array}$$

10. Make a ten to add. Add the other number to find the sum.

$\textcircled{7} + \textcircled{3} + 3 =$ _____

$\boxed{}$

STOP

Chapter Test, Form 3A

Write the correct answer.
Circle the greater number. Count on to add.

1. $5 + 2 =$ _____

2. $8 + 2 =$ _____

Use the number line to add. Write the sum.

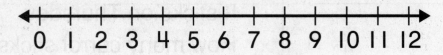

$$\begin{array}{ccccccccccccc} 0 & 1 & 2 & 3 & 4 & 5 & 6 & 7 & 8 & 9 & 10 & 11 & 12 \end{array}$$

3. $7 + 3 =$ _____

4.
$$\begin{array}{r} 9 \\ + 3 \\ \hline \square \end{array}$$

Find the sum.

5. $4 + 4 =$ _____

6.
$$\begin{array}{r} 7 \\ + 8 \\ \hline \square \end{array}$$

7. Write a doubles fact that will help you find the sum of $7 + 8$.

_____ + _____ = _____

8. Make a ten to add. Write the missing numbers.

$$\begin{array}{r} 7 \\ + 6 \\ \hline \square \end{array} \longrightarrow \begin{array}{r} 10 \\ + \square \\ \hline \square \end{array}$$

GO on

Chapter Test, Form 3A   *(continued)*

Write the correct answer.

9. Write the addends. Add.

_____ + _____ = _____   _____ + _____ = _____

---

10. Make a ten. Write that number. Add the other number to find the sum.

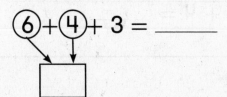

6 + 4 + 3 = _____

Write the addition number sentence and solve.

11. One ladybug has 6 dots. The other ladybug has 3 dots. How many dots do they have altogether?

_____ + _____ = _____ dots

12. 4 frogs jump into the pond. 3 sit on the log. How many frogs are there in all?

_____ + _____ = _____ frogs

---

13. Ava ate 2 slices of pizza for dinner. She also ate 2 carrots and 1 apple. How many pieces of food did Ava eat in all?

_____ + _____ + _____ = _____

Chapter Test, Form 3B

Write the correct answer.
Circle the greater number. Count on to add.

1. $2 + 6 =$ _____

2. $3 + 1 =$ _____

Use the number line to add. Write the sum.

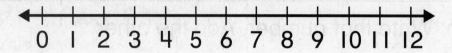

3. $5 + 3 =$ _____

4. $6 + 4 =$ _____

Write the sum.

5.
$$\begin{array}{r} 6 \\ + 6 \\ \hline \square \end{array}$$

6.
$$\begin{array}{r} 4 \\ + 5 \\ \hline \square \end{array}$$

7. Write a doubles fact that will help you find the sum of $8 + 9$.

_____ + _____ = _____

8. Make a ten to add. Write the missing numbers.

$$\begin{array}{r} 8 \\ + 4 \\ \hline \square \end{array} \longrightarrow \begin{array}{r} 10 \\ + \square \\ \hline \square \end{array}$$

GO on

Grade 1 • Chapter 3 Addition Strategies to 20

Name _____

Chapter Test, Form 3B   (continued)

Write the correct answer.

9. Write the addends. Add.

____ + ____ = ____   ____ + ____ = ____

_____

10. Add the doubles. Write that number. Add the
other number to find the sum.

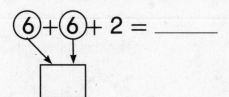

_____

Write the addition number sentence and solve.

11. Tom sees 5 red bikes. He sees 2 blue bikes. How many bikes are there in all?	**12.** 6 children play tag. 3 play hide-and-seek. How many children are playing?
___ + ___ = ___ bikes	___ + ___ = ___ children

13. 7 children walked to school. The same number
of children rode the bus. How many children
are there in all?

____ + ____ = ____ children

Name _____

Standardized Test Practice

Listen as your teacher reads each problem. Choose the correct answer.

Example A

Start with the greater number. Count on to add.

$4 + 2 =$ _____

- ○ 4
- ○ 5
- ○ 6
- ○ 7

Example B

Find the sum.

$4 + 4 =$ _____

- ○ 7
- ○ 9
- ○ 8
- ○ 10

---

1. Use the number line to add. What is the sum?

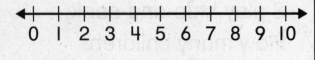

$7 + 2 =$ _____

- ○ 7
- ○ 8
- ○ 9
- ○ 10

2. Rose had 5 pennies. She got 2 more. How many pennies does Rose have now?

- ○ 4
- ○ 5
- ○ 6
- ○ 7

GO on

Standardized Test Practice (continued)

**Listen as your teacher reads each problem.
Choose the correct answer.**

3. Add.

$$5 + 6 = \underline{\hphantom{000}}$$

○ 11   ○ 10

○ 9   ○ 8

4. What is the sum?

$$\begin{array}{r} 5 \\ + 5 \\ \hline \end{array}$$

○ 0   ○ 10

○ 25   ○ 30

5. Count on to add.

$$4 + 3 = \underline{\hphantom{000}}$$

○ 4

○ 5

○ 6

○ 7

6. Which addends match the picture?

○ 2 + 3; 3 + 2

○ 3 + 4; 4 + 3

○ 4 + 2; 2 + 4

○ 5 + 3; 3 + 5

7. Make a ten. Add the other number to find the sum.

$$5 + 5 + 4 = \underline{\hphantom{000}}$$

○ 12   ○ 13

○ 14   ○ 15

8. Add the doubles. Add the other number to find the sum. What is the sum?

$$\textcircled{6} + \textcircled{6} + 3 = \underline{\hphantom{000}}$$

○ 15   ○ 13

○ 11   ○ 9

STOP

Oral Assessment

Directions: This test targets those students who have developing verbal skills—both oral and written. Ask the questions below and have students record their answers, or record the answers they supply.

Preparation: Counters are needed for this assessment.

1. Say: *Write 2 + 6 = 8 another way.*

2. Ask: *What is 4 + 3? Count on to find the sum.*

3. Ask: *What is 8 + 1? Count on to find the sum.*

4. Say: *Ryan has 3 blue shirts and 5 red shirts. How many shirts does he have? Use ◯.*

5. Say: *Use the number line to help you add 9 + 2.*

6. Ask: *What is the sum of 2 + 2?*

7. Ask: *What is the sum of 5 + 5?*

8. Say: *Ami has 2 purple skirts. She also has 3 green skirts. How many skirts does she have? Use ◯.*

Notes

_____

_____

_____

Name _____

Oral Assessment
Student Recording Sheet

1. _____ 2. _____

3. _____ 4. _____

5. _____

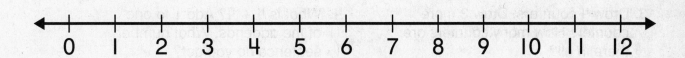

6. _____ 7. _____

8. _____

Name _____

 # Listening Assessment

Directions: Ask students to complete each of the tasks.

1. What is 5 + 2? Switch the two addends. Write both number sentences. Do you get the same answer?

2. Start with the number 6. Count on 3. What is the answer?

3. Draw 4 counters. Draw 3 more counters. How many counters are there in all?

4. What is 4 + 4? Add 1 to one of the addends. What number sentence do you get?

5. Start at 5 on the number line. Count on 3. What number are you on now? What is 5 + 3?

Notes

_____

_____

_____

Name _____

 Listening Assessment
Student Recording Sheet

1. _____ + _____ = _____   _____ + _____ = _____

   Yes   No

2. _____

3.

   _____

4. _____

   _____ + _____ = _____   or   _____ + _____ = _____

5. ◄———┼———┼———┼———┼———┼———┼———┼———┼———┼———┼———┼———┼———►
      0   1   2   3   4   5   6   7   8   9 10 11 12

   _____

   _____

Am I Ready?

Practice

Subtract.

1. 7 – 2 = _____

2. 8 – 1 = _____

3. 4 – 0 = _____

4. 10
  – 5
  ——

5. 6
  – 5
  ——

6. 5
  – 3
  ——

7. 9
  – 7
  ——

8. 7
  – 1
  ——

9. 2
  – 0
  ——

10. Cross out 3 trucks. Use the pictures
to write a subtraction number sentence.

 ◯ ◯

Am I Ready?

Review

You can use a number line to help you subtract.

$7 - 3 =$ _____

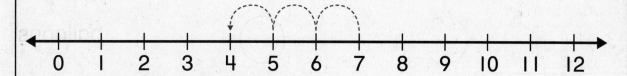

Start at 7 and count back 3.
You will end up on 4. The answer is 4.

$7 - 3 =$ _____

Subtract. Use the number line to count back.

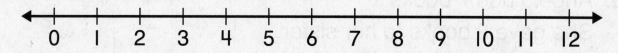

1. $5 - 3 =$ _____

2. $8 - 2 =$ _____

3. $3 - 0 =$ _____

4. $\begin{array}{r} 10 \\ -\ 3 \\ \hline \end{array}$ **5.** $\begin{array}{r} 6 \\ -\ 2 \\ \hline \end{array}$ **6.** $\begin{array}{r} 2 \\ -\ 1 \\ \hline \end{array}$

Name _____

Am I Ready?

Apply

Write a number sentence to solve.

1. Steve had 8 balloons.

    3 balloons popped.

    How many balloons does Steve have left?

    _____ ◯ _____ ◯ _____ balloons

2. There are 10 people in the swimming pool.

    6 people get out of the pool.

    How many people are in the pool now?

    _____ ◯ _____ ◯ _____ people

3. Angela had 7 books.

    She gave 2 books to her sister.

    How many books does Angela have left?

    _____ ◯ _____ ◯ _____ books

4. There were 4 rabbits in the yard.

    1 rabbit ran away.

    How many rabbits are in the yard now?

    _____ ◯ _____ ◯ _____ rabbits

Name _____

Diagnostic Test

Am I Ready for the Chapter?

1. Circle the equal sign.

     +   −   =

2. Circle the minus sign.

     +   −   =

Subtract.

3.   5
      − 2
     ―――

4.   8
      − 3
     ―――

5.   6
      − 5
     ―――

6.   4
      − 0
     ―――

7.   9
      − 6
     ―――

8.   7
      − 5
     ―――

9.   2
      − 1
     ―――

10.   3
      − 3
     ―――

11.   5
      − 4
     ―――

Cross out three boats. Use the pictures to write a subtraction number sentence.

12.

_____ ◯ _____ ◯ _____

Name _____

Pretest

Listen to the directions. Write the answer.

1. Count back to subtract.

   Start with 4.

   4, _____, _____

   $4 - 2 =$ _____

2. Write a number sentence to solve.
   Fran's mother cut 10 pieces of cake.
   There are 2 pieces left over.
   How many pieces of cake were eaten?

    pieces

3. Use the number line to help you subtract.

   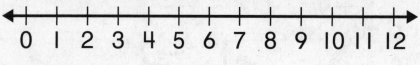

   $11 - 3 =$ _____

4. Add the doubles fact. Then subtract.

   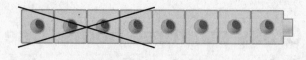

   $4 + 4 =$ _____ $8 - 4 =$ _____

5. Add and subtract. Complete the fact family.

   $6 + 5 =$ _____ $5 + 6 =$ _____

   $11 - 6 =$ _____ $11 - 5 =$ _____

Check My Progress *(Lessons 1 through 4)*

Count back to subtract.

1. 6
  − 2
  □

2. 9
  − 4
  □

3. 10
  − 3
  □

Use the number line to help you subtract. Write the difference.

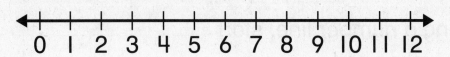

4. 11
  − 4

5. 9
  − 3

6. 8
  − 2

Add the doubles facts. Then subtract.

7. 5   10
  + 5   − 5

8. 8   16
  + 8   − 8

Write a subtraction number sentence to solve.

9. Harrison and his mom baked 12 cookies. They ate 4 cookies. How many cookies do they have left?

_____ − _____ = _____ cookies

Name _____

Vocabulary Test

Use the words in the box. Write your answers.

count back	fact family	missing addend

I. Addition and subtraction sentences that use the same numbers are a _____.

2. You can use related facts to find a _____.

3. To subtract using a number line, start at the greater number and _____.

Match the picture to its name.

4. 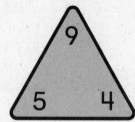 $5 + 4 = 9$ $9 - 5 = 4$ count back
$4 + 5 = 9$ $9 - 4 = 5$

5. $5 +$ ▢ $= 9$ fact family

6. 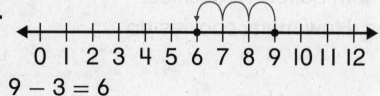   missing addend
$9 - 3 = 6$

Chapter Test, Form 1A

Circle the correct answer.

1. Count back to subtract.
Start with 5.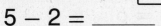

$5 - 2 =$ _____

A. 7   **B.** 3   **C.** 2

2.

```
<---+---+---+---+---+--->
    1   2   3   4   5
```

Use the number line to subtract. What
is the difference?

$4 - 2 =$ _____

F. 6   **G.** 4   **H.** 2

3. Add the doubles fact. Then subtract.

$4 + 4 = 8$ $8 - 4 =$ _____

A. 2   **B.** 3   **C.** 4

4. Take apart the number to make a 10. Then subtract.

$14 - 7$

    4   3

$14 - 4 = 10$

$10 - 3 =$ _____

F. 7   **G.** 6   **H.** 5

GO on

Chapter Test, Form 1A *(continued)*

5. What is the missing addend?

Part	Part
7	_____
Whole	
12	

$7 + \boxed{} = 12$

$12 - 7 = \boxed{}$

A. 5

B. 6

C. 7

6. What is the related subtraction fact?

$6 + 2 = 8$

F. $8 - 2 = 6$

G. $10 - 8 = 2$

H. $6 - 2 = 4$

7. What is the missing addend?

Part	Part
5	_____
Whole	
10	

$5 + \boxed{} = 10$

$10 - 5 = \boxed{}$

A. 6

B. 5

C. 4

8. What is the related addition fact?

$9 - 6 = 3$

F. $9 + 6 = 15$

G. $6 + 3 = 9$

H. $9 + 3 = 12$

STOP

Name _____

Chapter Test, Form IB

Circle the correct answer.

I. Count back to subtract.
Start with 7.
7 − 3 = _____

A. 2   **B.** 4   **C.** 6

2.

```
<---+---+---+---+---+---+--->
    1   2   3   4   5   6
```

Use the number line to subtract.
What is the difference?
6 − 3 = _____

F. 3   **G.** 5   **H.** 9

3. Add the doubles fact. Then subtract.

3 + 3 = 6   6 − 3 = _____

A. I   **B.** 2   **C.** 3

4. Take apart the number to make a 10. Then subtract.

11 − 2

```
  /  \
[ I ] [ I ]
```

11 − 1 = 10
10 − 1 = _____

F. 10   **G.** 9   **H.** 8

GO on

Chapter Test, Form I B *(continued)*

5. What is the missing addend?

Part	Part
2	_____
Whole	
9	

$2 + \boxed{} = 9$

$9 - 2 = \boxed{}$

A. 5

B. 6

C. 7

6. What is the related subtraction fact?

$5 + 2 = 7$

F. $9 - 7 = 2$

G. $5 - 2 = 3$

H. $7 - 5 = 2$

7. What is the missing addend?

Part	Part
3	_____
Whole	
9	

$3 + \boxed{} = 9$

$9 - 3 = \boxed{}$

A. 5

B. 6

C. 7

8. What is the related addition fact?

$7 - 5 = 2$

F. $7 + 2 = 9$

G. $5 + 7 = 12$

H. $2 + 5 = 7$

STOP

Name _____

Chapter Test, Form 2A

Circle the correct answer.

1. Count back to subtract.
Start with 6.

$6 - 3 =$ _____

A. 3   **B.** 2

C. 1   **D.** 0

2. Use the number line to subtract. What is the difference?

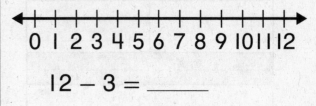

$12 - 3 =$ _____

F. 5   **G.** 6

H. 7   **I.** 9

3. Add the doubles fact.
Then subtract.

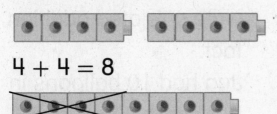

$4 + 4 = 8$

$8 - 4 =$ _____

A. 4   **B.** 5

C. 6   **D.** 7

4. Take apart the number to make a 10. Then subtract.

$16 - 9$

$\boxed{6}$ $\boxed{3}$

$16 - 6 = 10$

$10 - 3 =$ _____

A. 6   **B.** 7

C. 8   **D.** 9

GO on

Chapter Test, Form 2A (continued)

Write the correct answer.

5. Find the missing addend.

Part	Part
7	_____
Whole	
13	

$7 + \boxed{} = 13$

$13 - 7 = \boxed{}$

6. Use related facts to add and subtract.

$5 + 9 = $ _____

$14 - 5 = $ _____

7. Subtract. Write an addition fact to check your subtraction.

$15 - 7 = $ _____

_____ + _____ = _____

8. Write a subtraction number sentence. Then write a related addition fact.

Jan had 10 balloons in her hand. 4 balloons blew away. How many balloons does Jan have now?

_____ − _____ = _____ .

_____ + _____ = _____

Chapter Test, Form 2B

Circle the correct answer.

1. Count back to subtract. Start with 7.

$7 - 2 =$ _____

A. 2   **B.** 3

C. 4   **D.** 5

2. Use the number line to subtract. What is the difference?

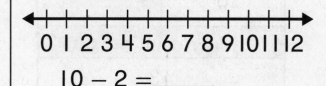

0 1 2 3 4 5 6 7 8 9 10 11 12

$10 - 2 =$ _____

F. 5   **G.** 6

H. 7   **I.** 8

3. Add the doubles fact. Then subtract.

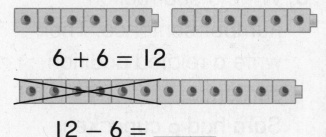

$6 + 6 = 12$

$12 - 6 =$ _____

A. 4   **B.** 5

C. 6   **D.** 7

4. Take apart the number to make a 10. Subtract.

13 − 6

3   3

$13 - 3 = 10$

$10 - 3 =$ _____

F. 9   **G.** 8

H. 7   **I.** 6

GO on

Chapter Test, Form 2B *(continued)*

Write the correct answer.

5. Find the missing addend.

Part	Part
9	_____
Whole	
13	

9 + ☐ = 13

13 − 9 = ☐

6. Use related facts to add and subtract.

7 + 6 = _____

13 − 7 = _____

7. Subtract. Write an addition fact to check your subtraction.

15 − 6 = _____

_____ + _____ = _____

8. Write a subtraction number sentence. Then write a related addition sentence.

Sara had 6 cupcakes. She gave 4 to friends. How many cupcakes does Sara have now?

_____ − _____ = _____

_____ + _____ = _____

Chapter Test, Form 3A

Write the correct answer.

1. Count back to subtract. Start with 6.

6, _____, _____

6 − 2 = _____

2. Use the number line to subtract. Write the difference.

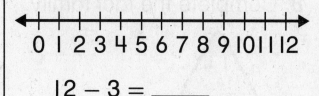

12 − 3 = _____

3. Add the doubles fact. Then subtract.

8 + 8 = _____

16 − 8 = _____

4. Use related facts to add and subtract.

9 + 8 = _____

17 − 8 = _____

5. Take apart the number to make a 10. Then subtract.

15 − 6

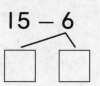

15 − _____ = 10

10 − 1 = _____

6. Complete the fact family.

9 + 2 = ☐   11 − 9 = ☐

2 + 9 = ☐   11 − 2 = ☐

GO on

Chapter Test, Form 3A *(continued)*

7. $8 + 4 = 12$. Write a related subtraction fact.

____ ◯ ____ ◯ ____

8. Complete the fact family.

$4 + 7 = \boxed{}$ $11 - 4 = \boxed{}$

$7 + 4 = \boxed{}$ $11 - 7 = \boxed{}$

9. Find the missing addend.

Part	Part
9	_____
Whole	
13	

$9 + \boxed{} = 13$

$13 - 9 = \boxed{}$

10. Subtract. Write an addition fact to check your subtraction.

$17 - 8 =$ _____

_____ $+$ _____ $=$ _____

Grade 1 • Chapter 4 Subtraction Strategies to 20

Chapter Test, Form 3B

Write the correct answer.

1. Count back to subtract. Start with 7.

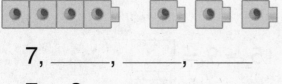

7, _____, _____, _____

7 − 3 = _____

2. Use the number line to subtract. Write the difference.

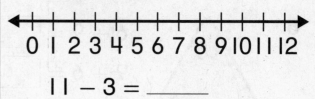

11 − 3 = _____

3. Add the doubles fact. Then subtract.

9 + 9 = _____

18 − 9 = _____

4. Use related facts to add and subtract.

8 + 5 = _____

13 − 8 = _____

5. Take apart the number to make a 10. Then subtract.

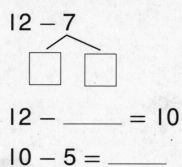

12 − _____ = 10

10 − 5 = _____

6. Complete the fact family.

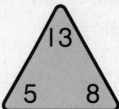

8 + 5 = ☐   13 − 8 = ☐

5 + 8 = ☐   13 − 5 = ☐

GO on

Chapter Test, Form 3B   *(continued)*

7. $6 + 5 = 11$. Write a related subtraction fact.

_____ ◯ _____ ◯ _____

8.

$6 + 9 = \boxed{}$ $15 - 9 = \boxed{}$

$9 + 6 = \boxed{}$ $15 - 6 = \boxed{}$

9. Find the missing addends.

Part	Part
4	_____
Whole	
13	

$4 + \boxed{} = 13$

$13 - 4 = \boxed{}$

10. Subtract. Write an addition fact to check your subtraction.

$14 - 8 =$ _____

_____ $+$ _____ $=$ _____

Standardized Test Practice

Listen as your teacher reads each problem.
Choose the correct answer.

Example A

Count back to subtract.
Start with 5.

$5 - 2 =$ _____

○ 3   ○ 2

○ I   ○ 0

Example B

Use the number line to subtract. What is the difference?

$9 - 2 =$ _____

○ 7   ○ 6

○ 5   ○ 4

I. Add the doubles fact.
Then subtract. Which number shows the difference?

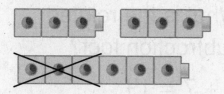

$3 + 3 = 6$

$6 - 3 =$ _____

○ 4   ○ 3

○ 2   ○ I

2. Which subtraction number sentence goes with the story?

Kris sees 7 fish. 6 fish swim away. How many fish are left?

○ $7 - 3 = 4$

○ $7 - 6 = 1$

○ $7 - 5 = 2$

○ $6 + 1 = 7$

GO on

Name _____

Standardized Test Practice (continued)

**Listen as your teacher reads each problem.
Choose the correct answer.**

3. Complete the fact family.

$5 + 4 = \boxed{9}$

$4 + 5 = \boxed{9}$

$9 - 4 = \boxed{5}$

○ $9 - 3 = 6$

○ $9 + 5 = 14$

○ $9 - 5 = 4$

○ $9 - 2 = 7$

4. What is the related subtraction fact?

$5 + 2 = 7$

○ $9 - 7 = 2$

○ $9 - 5 = 4$

○ $5 - 2 = 3$

○ $7 - 5 = 2$

5.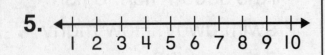

Use the number line to subtract.

$8 - 3 = $ _____

○ 7   ○ 6

○ 5   ○ 4

6. What is the related subtraction fact?

$7 + 7 = 14$

○ $14 - 7 = 7$

○ $15 - 9 = 6$

○ $16 - 8 = 8$

○ $17 - 9 = 6$

Name _____

 # Oral Assessment

Preparation: Connecting cubes and board access are needed for this assessment.

Directions: This test targets those students who have developing verbal skills—both oral and written. Ask the questions below and have students record their answers, or record the answers they supply.

1. Show the students 10 cubes. Have the students count the cubes. Ask: *How many cubes are there?* Tell the students you are going to take some of the cubes away. Take away 2 of the cubes. Say: *Count back to find how many cubes are left. Write the answer.*

2. Draw 5 circles on the board. Ask: *How many circles did I draw?* Put an *X* through 3 of the circles. Ask: *How many circles did I cross out? Write the subtraction number sentence.*

3. Draw a number line on the board. Number it from 0 to 5. Circle the number five. Then, show a line bouncing from 5 to 4 to 3. Show a bold dot on the line above the number 3. Have the student write the subtraction number sentence.

4. Say: *You are going to solve a problem by crossing out parts of the picture.* Say: *There are 8 apples in the cafeteria. Students eat 5 of them. How many are left?*

5. Draw 12 stars on the board. Then cross out 3 of the stars. Say: *Write a subtraction number sentence to solve this problem.*

6. Show students 2 rows of 4 connecting cubes. Say: *You can use doubles to add or subtract. Use the cubes to help you write and solve an addition and a subtraction problem.*

7. Write the addition problem on the board, $7 + 4 =$ _____.
Say: *Solve this addition problem.* Then say: *Write a related subtraction fact.*

8. Draw a triangle on the board. Write a 10 in the top of the triangle. Write a 2 in the left corner. Write an 8 in the right corner. Have students complete the fact family for this drawing.

Notes

_____

_____

_____

Name _____

 Oral Assessment Response Sheet

1. _____ _____

2. _____ ◯ _____ ◯ _____

3. _____ ◯ _____ ◯ _____

4. 🍎🍎🍎🍎🍎🍎🍎🍎

   _____ apples

5. _____ ◯ _____ ◯ _____

6. _____ ◯ _____ ◯ _____
   _____ ◯ _____ ◯ _____

7. _____
   _____ ◯ _____ ◯ _____
   or
   _____ ◯ _____ ◯ _____

8. $8 + 2 = \boxed{}$ $10 - 8 = \boxed{}$

   $2 + 8 = \boxed{}$ $10 - 2 = \boxed{}$

Name _____

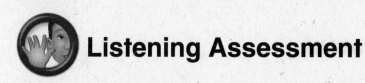 **Listening Assessment**

Preparation: Connecting cubes are needed for this assessment.

Directions: Ask students to complete each of the following groups of tasks.

I. Draw six squares. Cross out two squares. Write the number sentence, and count back to solve.

2. Draw eight stars. Cross out five stars. Write a subtraction number sentence to solve.

3. Draw a number line. Number it from 1–10. Use the number line to solve 6 minus 2.

4. Draw a picture to show 9–1. Write the difference.

5. Show 12 minus 3 with connecting cubes. What is the difference? Write it.

6. Show 6 + 6 with connecting cubes. Write the sum. Show 12 − 6 with connecting cubes. Write the difference.

Notes

_____

_____

_____

Name _____

 **Listening Assessment
Response Sheet**

1. _____

___ ◯ ___ ◯ ___

2. _____

___ ◯ ___ ◯ ___

3. _____

6 − 2 = ____

4. _____

9 − 1 = ____

5. _____ _____

_____ _____

6. _____ ____

_____ ____

Name _____

Am I Ready?

Practice

Circle to make groups of 10.

1.

2.

Write the missing numbers.

3.

1	2		4	5	6	7	8	9	10
11	12	13		15	16	17		19	20
21		23	24	25	26	27	28	29	

Solve.

4. Each bowl has 10 plums in it. There are
   5 bowls on the table. How many plums in all?
   _____ plums

Am I Ready?

Review

Count ten items. Circle the group of ten.

Circle groups of 10.

1.

2.

3.

Am I Ready?

Solve. Write your answer.

1. Each bowl has 10 apples in it. There are 4 bowls on the table. How many apples are there in all?

_____ apples

2. Each box at the book fair had 10 books in it. 9 boxes of books were sold. How many books were sold?

_____ books

3. Ron has 10 CDs. Sandra has 10 CDs. Ari has 10 CDs. How many CDs do they have altogether?

_____ CDs

4. Kim sorted her marbles into groups of 10. She had 2 groups of 10, plus 5 marbles left over. How many marbles does Kim have in all?

_____ marbles

5. Marc put carrots in bags for snack time. He put 10 carrots in each bag. Marc filled 5 bags and had 3 carrots left over. How many carrots did Marc have in all?

_____ carrots

Diagnostic Test

Am I Ready for the Chapter?

Circle to make groups of 10.

1.

2.

3. Write the missing numbers.

1	2			5	6		8		10
11			14		16	17	18		

Circle groups of 10. Write the number.

4.

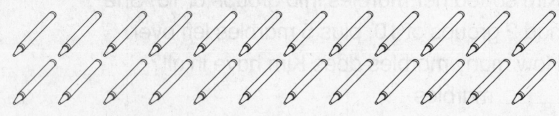

_____ crayons

5. Amy has 3 boxes of crayons. There are 10 crayons in each box. How many crayons does Amy have in all? _____ crayons

Name _____

Pretest

Write the correct answer.

1. Write how many tens and how many more. Then write the number.

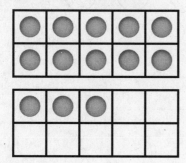

_____ ten and _____ more is _____.

2. Write how many tens and ones. Write how many in all.

_____ ten and _____ ones = _____

3. Count by tens. Write the numbers. Write how much in all.

_____ ¢ _____ ¢ _____ ¢
in all

4. Count the groups of tens and ones. Write the number.

tens	ones

tens	ones
2	7

_____
twenty-seven

5. Write the missing number.

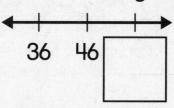

36   46   [ ]

6. Compare. Write >, <, or =.

1 ◯ 50

Name _____

Check My Progress (Lessons 1 through 4)

Write how many tens and ones. Write how many in all.

1.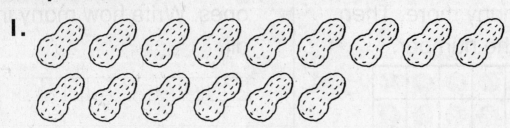

   _____ ten and _____ ones = _____

2. Write the missing number.

   109, 110, 111, _____, 113

Count groups of ten. Write the number.

3.

   _____ tens = _____

4.

   _____ tens = _____

5.

   _____ tens and _____ more is _____.

Grade 1 • Chapter 5 Place Value

Check My Progress   (Lessons 5 through 11)

Write the number that is ten more.

1. 17, _____   **2.** 89, _____   **3.** 2, _____

Write the number that is ten less.

4. 56, _____   **5.** 39, _____   **6.** 72, _____

7. Write the missing number.

97, 98, 99, _____, 101, 102

8. Count the groups of ten. Write the number.

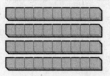

_____ tens = _____

Write >, <, or =.

9. 21 ◯ 19   **10.** 34 ◯ 39

11. 17 ◯ 17   **12.** 51 ◯ 50

13. Ginny has 24 dolls. How many tens and ones does she have?

_____ tens _____ ones

Name _____

Vocabulary Test

Choose a word from the box to complete each sentence.

equal to (=)	greater than (>)	less than (<)
ones	regroup	tens

1. The numbers in the range of 10 to 99 are

_____.

2. The number or group with fewer is _____.

3. When you take apart a number to write it in a new way,

you _____.

4. The numbers in the range of 0 to 9 are _____.

5. The number or group with more is _____.

6. _____ means is the same as.

Name _____

Chapter Test, Form 1A

Circle the correct answer.

1. Count by tens. What is the number?

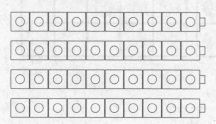

4 tens = _____
forty

A. 20

B. 40

C. 60

2. Count. How many tens and ones?

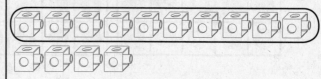

F. 1 ten and 4 ones

G. 3 tens and 4 ones

H. 4 tens and 1 one

3. What is the number?

tens	ones		tens	ones
			2	5

twenty-five

A. 23

B. 24

C. 25

4. Which number is ten more?

28, _____

F. 32

G. 38

H. 44

GO on

Chapter Test, Form 1A   *(continued)*

5. Write how many tens and how many more.
Then write the number.

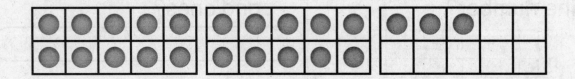

_____ ten and _____ more is _____.

A. 2 tens and 3 more is 32

B. 2 tens and 3 more is 23

C. 3 tens and 2 more is 32

6. Compare. Choose >, <, or =.

tens	ones
6	5
5	4

65 ◯ 54

F. <   **G.** >   **H.** =

7. What is the missing number?

103, 104, 105, 106, 107, _____, 109

F. 104   **G.** 108   **H.** 110

Name _____

Chapter Test, Form 1B

Circle the correct answer.

1. Count by tens. What is the number?

5 tens = _____

fifty

A. 20

B. 40

C. 50

2. Count. How many tens and ones?

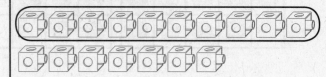

F. 1 ten and 6 ones

G. 7 tens and 1 one

H. 1 ten and 7 ones

3. What is the number?

tens	ones

tens	ones
3	5

_____

thirty-five

A. 25

B. 35

C. 53

4. Which number is ten less?

_____, 100

F. 80

G. 85

H. 90

GO on

Chapter Test, Form IB (continued)

5. Write how many tens and how many more.
Then write the number.

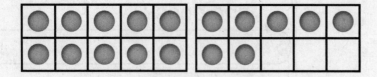

_____ ten and _____ more is _____.

A. I ten and 7 more is 17

B. 7 tens and I more is 71

C. I ten and 7 more is 71

6. Compare. Choose >, <, or =.

tens	ones
3	5
4	6

35 ◯ 46

F. <   **G.** >   **H.** =

7. What is the missing number?
115, 116, _____, 118, 119

A. 117   **B.** 127   **C.** 128

Name _____

Chapter Test, Form 2A

Circle the correct answer.

1. Count by tens. What is the number?

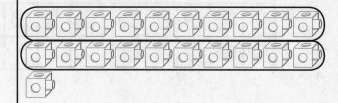

6 tens = _____

sixty

A. 70   **B.** 60

C. 50   **D.** 40

2. Count. How many tens and ones?

F. 3 tens and 1 one

G. 2 tens and 2 ones

H. 1 ten and 2 ones

I. 2 tens and 1 one

3. What is the number?

tens	ones	tens	ones
		5	2

fifty-two

A. 25   **B.** 35

C. 52   **D.** 53

4. Which number is ten more?

28, _____

F. 30

G. 35

H. 38

I. 39

GO on

Name _____

Chapter Test, Form 2A   *(continued)*

Write the correct answer.

5. Write how many tens and how many more.
Then write the number.

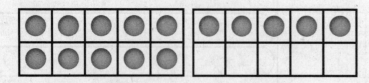

_____ ten and _____ more is _____.

6. Count by fives. Write the the numbers.
How much in all?

_____¢ _____¢ _____¢ _____¢
                                    in all

7. Write each number. Circle *is greater than*,
is less than, or *is equal to*.

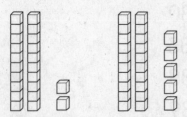

_____ is greater than _____
      is less than
      is equal to

Name _____

Chapter Test, Form 2B

Circle the correct answer.

1. Count by tens. What is the number?

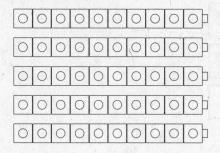

5 tens = _____
                  fifty

A. 70   **B.** 60

C. 50   **D.** 40

2. Count. How many tens and ones?

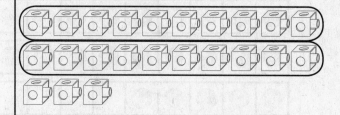

F. 3 tens and 1 one

G. 2 tens and 2 ones

H. 2 tens and 3 ones

I. 2 tens and 1 one

3. What is the number?

tens	ones

tens	ones
4	6

_____
forty-six

A. 40   **B.** 45

C. 46   **D.** 56

4. Which number is ten less?

_____, 73

F. 53

G. 60

H. 63

I. 69

Chapter Test, Form 2B   *(continued)*

Write the correct answer.

5. Write how many tens and how many more.
Then write the number.

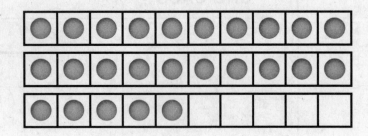

_____ tens and _____ more is _____ .

6. Count by fives. Write the numbers. How much in all?

_____¢ _____¢ _____¢
in all

7. Write each number. Circle *is greater than*,
is less than, or *is equal to*.

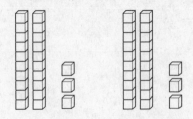

_____ is greater than _____
       is less than
       is equal to

STOP

Name _____

Chapter Test, Form 3A

Write the correct answer.

1. Count by tens. Write the number.

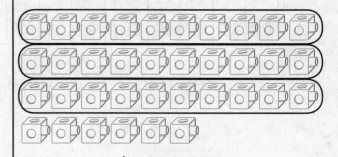

7 tens = _____
seventy

2. Count. Write the numbers.

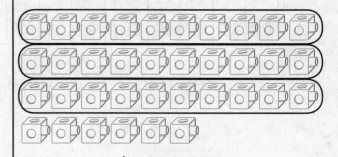

_____ tens and _____ more is _____.

3. What is the number?

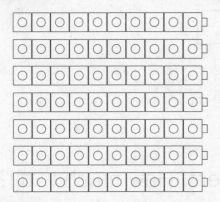

tens	ones		tens	ones

_____
twenty-eight

4. Write the numbers that are ten more and ten less than the number.

_____, 32, _____

5. Count by tens. Write the numbers. How much in all?

_____¢   _____¢   _____¢   _____¢
in all

6. Compare. Write >, <, or =.

43 ◯ 34

GO on

7. Count. Write the numbers.

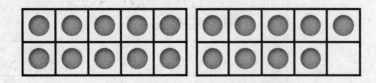

_____ ten and _____ more is _____.

8. Count by fives. Write the numbers. How much in all?

_____ ¢ _____ ¢ _____ ¢ _____ ¢ _____ ¢

in all

9. Write the number in two ways.

hundreds	tens	ones

hundreds	tens	ones
_____	_____	_____

_____
one hundred six

STOP

Name _____

Chapter Test, Form 3B

Write the correct answer.

1. Count by tens. Write the number.

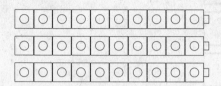

3 tens = _____
         thirty

2. Count. Write the numbers.

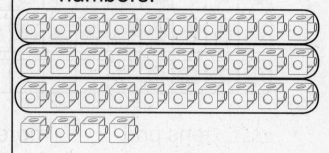

_____ tens and _____ ones

3. Write the numbers.

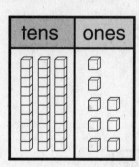

tens	ones		tens	ones
			____	____

_____
thirty-eight

4. Write the numbers that are ten more and ten less than the number.

_____, 43, _____

5. Count by tens. Write the numbers. How much in all?

___¢   ___¢   ___¢
                in all

6. Compare. Write >, <, or =.

45 ◯ 75

GO on

Chapter Test, Form 3B *(continued)*

7. Count. Write the numbers.

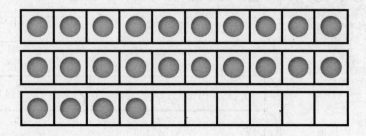

_____ tens and _____ more is _____.

8. Count by fives. Write the numbers. How much in all?

_____ ¢ _____ ¢ _____ ¢ _____ ¢

in all

9. Write the number in two ways.

hundreds	tens	ones

hundreds	tens	ones
_____	___	___

_____

one hundred twelve

STOP

Name _____

Standardized Test Practice

Listen as your teacher reads each problem.
Choose the correct answer.

Example A

Count by tens. What is the number?

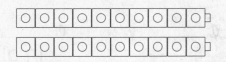

2 tens = _____
         twenty

○ 20   ○ 40
○ 60   ○ 80

Example B

What is the number?

tens	ones

tens	ones
4	3

○ 43   ○ 34
○ 25   ○ 24

I. What is the missing number?

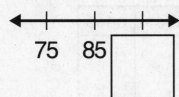

75   85   ▢

○ 86
○ 90
○ 95
○ 97

2. Count from 29 to 35. What number comes next?

1	2	3	4	5	6	7	8	9	10
11	12	13	14	15	16	17	18	19	20
21	22	23	24	25	26	27	28	29	30
31	32	33	34	35	36	37	38	39	40

○ 36   ○ 29
○ 38   ○ 19

GO on

Standardized Test Practice *(continued)*

Listen as your teacher reads each problem.
Choose the correct answer.

3. Which number is ten more?

24, _____

- ○ 28
- ○ 34
- ○ 30
- ○ 38

4. Count by fives. How much in all?

_____ ¢ _____ ¢ _____ ¢ _____ ¢

in all

- ○ 40¢
- ○ 20¢
- ○ 30¢
- ○ 15¢

5. Marcy is thinking of a number. It has 8 groups of ten and nine more. What is the number?

- ○ 69
- ○ 79
- ○ 89
- ○ 98

6. What is the number?

hundreds	tens	ones

hundreds	tens	ones
___	___	___

_____

one hundred twenty-four

- ○ 104
- ○ 124
- ○ 114
- ○ 142

Oral Assessment

Preparation: Connecting cubes and dimes are needed for this assessment.

Directions: This test targets those students who have developing verbal skills—both oral and written. Ask the questions below and have students record their answers, or record the answers they supply.

1. Show students 2 trains with 10 connecting cubes each. Ask: *How many tens are there?*

2. Show students 3 trains with 10 connecting cubes each and 4 single connecting cubes. Ask: *How many tens are there? How many ones are there? What is the number?*

3. Set 6 dimes in front of the student. Ask the student to count by tens. Say: *How much in all?*

4. Write the number 31 on the board. Ask: *What numbers are ten more and ten less than 31? Write the numbers.*

5. Show students 23 connecting cubes and 32 connecting cubes. Ask: *Which pile is greater?*

6. Ask: *What numbers are ten more and ten less than 108? Write the numbers.*

Notes

_____

_____

_____

_____

_____

_____

Oral Assessment Response Sheet

1. _____   **2.** ____ tens ____ ones

    _____

3. _____   **4.** _____

5. _____

6. _____

Name _____

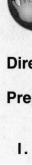

Listening Assessment

Directions: Ask students to perform the following tasks.

Preparation: Base-10 blocks and nickels are needed for this assessment.

1. Show three base-10 rods. Write how many tens. Write the number.

2. Show four base-10 rods and two unit cubes.
   Write how many tens.
   Write how many ones.
   Write the number.

3. Set 5 nickels on the table. Count by fives. How much money altogether?

4. Write a number that is less than 10. Write a number that is greater than 10.

5. Show the number 111 using the base-10 blocks. Write how many hundreds, tens, and ones.

Notes

_____

_____

_____

_____

Name _____

 Listening Assessment Response Sheet

1. _____ tens

2. _____ tens and

_____ ones

3. _____

4. _____

_____

_____

_____

_____

5. _____

Name _____

Am I Ready?

Practice

Write how many tens and ones.

1.

   _____ tens _____ ones = _____

2.

   _____ tens _____ ones = _____

Add.

3. $15 + 3 =$ _____   4. $7 + 4 =$ _____

Subtract.

5. $\begin{array}{r} 8 \\ -2 \\ \hline \end{array}$ 6. $\begin{array}{r} 17 \\ -5 \\ \hline \end{array}$ 7. $\begin{array}{r} 11 \\ -1 \\ \hline \end{array}$

8. Pedro painted 17 pictures. He gave
   3 pictures to his mom. How many pictures
   does he have left? _____ pictures

Am I Ready?

Review

You can find the difference by counting back.

Find 5 − 3.

Start at 5. Count back 3.

2

$5 - 3 =$ _____

Find 8 − 2.

Start at 8. Count back 2.

7, 6

$8 - 2 =$ _____

Count back to subtract. Write the difference.

1. $6 - 3 =$ _____

2. $5 - 1 =$ _____

3. $8 - 3 =$ _____

4. $4 - 3 =$ _____

5. $9 - 3 =$ _____

6. $7 - 1 =$ _____

Am I Ready?

Apply

Solve.

1. There were 20 rabbits eating carrots. 9 rabbits hopped away. How many rabbits are left?

_____ rabbits

2. 49 people were on a train. 10 people got off. How many people are on the train now?

_____ people

3. Sam had 55 apples. He sold 3 apples. How many apples does Sam have left?

_____ apples

4. There were 99 snowflakes on a window. 50 of the snowflakes melted. How many snowflakes are still on the window?

_____ snowflakes

5. Fatima is reading a book that has 80 pages. She has already read 9 pages. How many pages does Fatima have left to read?

_____ pages

Diagnostic Test

Am I Ready for the Chapter?

Write how many tens and ones.

1.

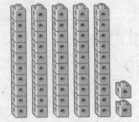

_____ tens _____ ones = _____

2.

_____ tens _____ ones = _____

Add.

3. $5 + 4 =$ _____

4. $8 + 2 =$ _____

Subtract.

5. 11
    − 5
    ___

6. 10
    − 3
    ___

7. 12
    − 6
    ___

8. 14
    − 4
    ___

9. Liz ran 3 miles and walked 1 mile. How many more miles did she run than walk?

_____ miles

Name _____

Pretest

Write the correct answer.

1. 4 tens + 2 tens

= _____ tens

40 + 20 = _____

2. Count on to add. Write the sum.

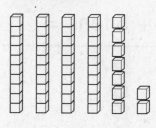

47 + 2 = _____

3. Add.

tens	ones
1	6
+	3

4. Circle the ones to show regrouping. Write your answer.

tens	ones

15 + 5 = _____

5. Subtract.

6 tens − 1 ten

= _____ tens

60 − 10 = _____

6. Use the number line to subtract. Circle the number that you land on. Write the difference.

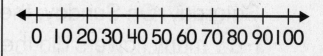

0 10 20 30 40 50 60 70 80 90 100

80 − 30 = _____

Name _____

Check My Progress *(Lessons 1 through 5)*

Count on to add. Write the sum.

1. 1 ten + 7 tens = _____ tens   10 + 70 = _____

2. 2 tens + 5 tens = _____ tens   20 + 50 = _____

3.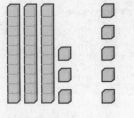

33 + 5 = _____

4.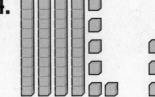

46 + 3 = _____

Add.

5.

tens	ones
3	3
+	6

6.

tens	ones
5	2
+	5

7.

tens	ones
2	5
+	4

8. Antonio scored 25 points on his video game. Caleb score 34 points. How many points did they score altogether?

_____ points

9. Molly helped her mom plant 42 flowers on Saturday. On Sunday, they planted 12 flowers. How many flowers did they plant in all?

_____ flowers

Name _____

Vocabulary Test

Use the words in the box. Write your answers.

add	difference	ones	subtract	sum

1. The answer to a subtraction problem is called the _____.

2. You _____ to find the sum.

3. In the number 64, 4 is in the _____ place.

4. The answer to an addition problem is called the _____.

5. You _____ to find the difference.

Name _____

Chapter Test, Form 1A

Circle the correct answer.

1. Add.

  3 tens   30
+ 4 tens   + 40
_____   _____

_____ tens

A. 7 tens; 70

B. 6 tens; 60

C. 5 tens; 50

2. Count on to add. What is the sum?

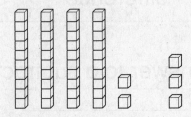

$42 + 3 =$ _____

F. 43   **G.** 45   **H.** 49

3. Add.

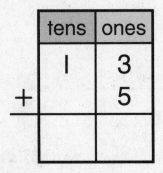

tens	ones
1	3
+	5

A. 14   **B.** 16   **C.** 18

4. What is the answer?

$19 + 9 =$ _____

tens	ones

F. 30   **G.** 29   **H.** 28

5. Subtract.

  9 tens   90
− 2 tens   − 20
_____   _____

_____ tens   _____

A. 4 tens; 40

B. 6 tens; 60

C. 7 tens; 70

GO on

Grade 1 • Chapter 6 Two-Digit Addition and Subtraction

Chapter Test, Form 1A *(continued)*

6. Use the number line to subtract. What is the difference?

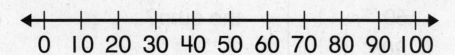

$90 - 40 =$ _____

F. 40   **G.** 50   **H.** 60

---

7. Use related facts to add and subtract.

$10 +$ _____ $= 30$

$30 - 10 =$ _____

A. 20; 20

B. 15; 15

C. 10; 10

8. Subtract. Which is the related addition fact?

$70 - 30 =$ _____

F. $40 + 20 = 60$

G. $30 + 30 = 60$

H. $30 + 40 = 70$

---

9. Ben has 40 stickers. He gives 30 stickers to his friend. How many stickers does Ben have left?

A. 20

B. 10

C. 5

10. There are 30 students in Mrs. Miller's class. 20 of them are girls. How many of them are boys?

F. 10

G. 15

H. 20

Name _____

Chapter Test, Form 1B

Circle the correct answer.

1. Add.

   6 tens   60
 + 2 tens   **+ 20**

_____ tens   _____

A. 7 tens; 70

B. 8 tens; 80

C. 9 tens; 90

2. Count on to add. What is the sum?

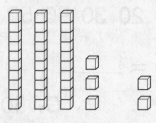

$33 + 2 =$ _____

F. 35 **G.** 45 **H.** 55

3. Add.

tens	ones
1	7
+	2

A. 20

B. 19

C. 18

4. What is the answer?

$13 + 7 =$ _____

tens	ones

F. 20 **G.** 29 **H.** 30

A. 4 tens; 40

B. 2 tens; 20

C. 1 tens; 10

5. Subtract.

   8 tens   80
 − 6 tens   **− 60**

_____ tens

GO on

Grade 1 · Chapter 6 Two-Digit Addition and Subtraction

Chapter Test, Form 1B *(continued)*

6. Use the number line to subtract. What is the difference?

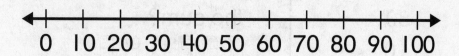

70 − 20 = _____

F. 30   **G.** 40   **H.** 50

---

7. Use related facts to add and subtract.

50 + _____ = 70

70 − 50 = _____

A. 20; 20

B. 15; 15

C. 10; 10

8. Subtract. Which is the related addition fact?

60 − 40 = _____

F. 40 + 20 = 60

G. 30 + 30 = 60

H. 30 + 40 = 70

---

9. Meg had 30 stickers. She gave 20 to her friend. How many stickers does Meg have left?

A. 9

B. 10

C. 12

10. There were 50 cups on a table. 20 cups were empty. How many cups were filled?

F. 30

G. 40

H. 73

Name _____

Chapter Test, Form 2A

Circle the correct answer.

1. Add.

    8 tens   80

  + 1 tens   + 10

  _____ tens   _____

A. 5 tens; 50

B. 7 tens; 70

C. 8 tens; 80

D. 9 tens; 90

2. Count on to add. What is the sum?

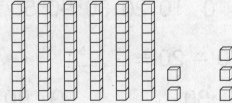

$62 + 3 =$ _____

F. 62   **G.** 65

H. 67   **I.** 69

3. Add.

tens	ones
2	6
+	2

A. 28   **B.** 25

C. 23   **D.** 21

4. What is the answer?

$19 + 4 =$ _____

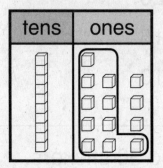

F. 33   **G.** 27

H. 23   **I.** 21

5. Subtract.

    6 tens   60

  − 3 tens   − 30

  _____ tens   _____

A. 4 tens; 40

B. 3 tens; 30

C. 2 tens; 20

D. 1 ten; 10

GO on

Chapter Test, Form 2A *(continued)*

Write the correct answer.

6. Use the number line to subtract. Circle the number that you land on. What is the difference?

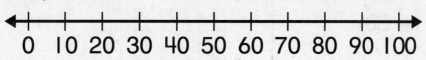

$$50 - 20 = \underline{\hspace{1cm}}$$

---

7. Use related facts to add and subtract.

$$20 + \underline{\hspace{1cm}} = 50$$
$$50 - 20 = \underline{\hspace{1cm}}$$

8. Subtract. Write a related addition fact.

$$70 - 30 = \underline{\hspace{1cm}}$$
$$\underline{\hspace{1cm}} + \underline{\hspace{1cm}} = \underline{\hspace{1cm}}$$

---

9. Write the subtraction number sentence. Then write a related addition fact.

Sam has 80 baseball cards. He gives 20 to his friend. How many cards does Sam have left?

$$\underline{\hspace{1cm}} - \underline{\hspace{1cm}} = \underline{\hspace{1cm}}$$
$$\underline{\hspace{1cm}} + \underline{\hspace{1cm}} = \underline{\hspace{1cm}}$$

10. Write the subtraction number sentence. Then write a related addition fact.

Corrie has 40 video games. She gives her brother 10 video games. How many video games does she have now?

$$\underline{\hspace{1cm}} - \underline{\hspace{1cm}} = \underline{\hspace{1cm}}$$
$$\underline{\hspace{1cm}} + \underline{\hspace{1cm}} = \underline{\hspace{1cm}}$$

STOP

Chapter Test, Form 2B

Circle the correct answer.

1. Add.

6 tens   60
+ 3 tens   + 30
_____ tens   _____

A. 5 tens; 50

B. 7 tens; 70

C. 8 tens; 80

D. 9 tens; 90

2. Count on to add. What is the sum?

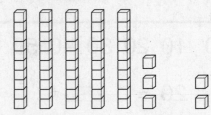

$53 + 2 =$ _____

F. 65   **G.** 55

H. 52   **I.** 42

3. Add.

tens	ones
3	4
+	2

A. 26   **B.** 36

C. 46   **D.** 56

4. What is the answer?

$24 + 8 =$ _____

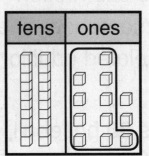

F. 33   **G.** 32

H. 23   **I.** 13

5. Subtract.

5 tens   50
− 1 tens   − 10
_____ tens   _____

A. 3 tens; 30

B. 4 tens; 40

C. 5 tens; 50

D. 6 tens; 60

GO on

Chapter Test, Form 2B *(continued)*

Write the correct answer.

6. Use the number line to subtract. Circle the number that you land on. What is the difference?

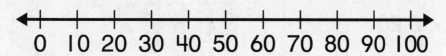

70 − 60 = _____

---

7. Use related facts to add and subtract.

50 + _____ = 70

70 − 50 = _____

8. Subtract. Write a related addition fact.

40 − 30 = _____

_____ + _____ = _____

---

9. Write the subtraction number sentence. Then write a related addition fact.

Kim has 50 shells from her trip to the ocean. She brought 20 to school. How many shells does Kim have at home?

_____ − _____ = _____

_____ + _____ = _____

10. Write the subtraction number sentence. Then write a related addition fact.

Jimmy has 50 toy cars. He lost 10 toy cars. How many toy cars does he have now?

_____ − _____ = _____

_____ + _____ = _____

STOP

Chapter Test, Form 3A

Write the correct answer.

1. Add.

7 tens	70
+ 2 tens	+ 20
____ tens	____

2. Count on to add. Write the sum.

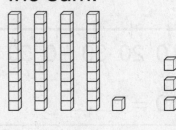

41 + 3 = _____

3. Add.

tens	ones
4	4
+	5

4. Circle the ones to show regrouping. Write your answer.

25 + 8 = _____

tens	ones

5. Subtract.

8 tens	80
− 4 tens	− 40
____ tens	____

6. Use the number line to subtract. Circle the number that you land on. What is the difference?

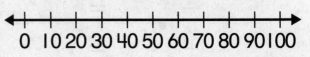

0 10 20 30 40 50 60 70 80 90 100

60 − 40 = _____

GO on

Grade 1 · Chapter 6 Two-Digit Addition and Subtraction

Chapter Test, Form 3A *(continued)*

Write the correct answer.

7. Use related facts to add and subtract.

$40 + \underline{\hspace{1.5cm}} = 70$

$70 - 40 = \underline{\hspace{1.5cm}}$

8. Subtract. Write a related addition fact.

$70 - 60 = \underline{\hspace{1.5cm}}$

$\underline{\hspace{1cm}} + \underline{\hspace{1cm}} = \underline{\hspace{1cm}}$

9. Write the subtraction number sentence. Then write a related addition fact.

Jeff caught 70 lightning bugs in a jar. He let 30 out of the jar. How many lightning bugs does Jeff have left?

$\underline{\hspace{1cm}} - \underline{\hspace{1cm}} = \underline{\hspace{1cm}}$

$\underline{\hspace{1cm}} + \underline{\hspace{1cm}} = \underline{\hspace{1cm}}$

10. Write the subtraction number sentence. Then write a related addition fact.

Ricky has 70 baseball cards. He gives 20 cards to his friend. How many cards does Ricky have left?

$\underline{\hspace{1cm}} - \underline{\hspace{1cm}} = \underline{\hspace{1cm}}$

$\underline{\hspace{1cm}} + \underline{\hspace{1cm}} = \underline{\hspace{1cm}}$

STOP

Chapter Test, Form 3B

Write the correct answer.

1. Add.

    8 tens   80

   + 1 tens   + 10

    _____ tens   _____

2. Count on to add. Write the sum.

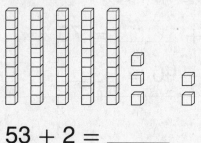

$53 + 2 =$ _____

---

3. Add.

tens	ones
7	2
+	6

4. Circle the ones to show regrouping. Write your answer.

$36 + 7 =$ _____

tens	ones

---

5. Subtract.

    4 tens   40

   − 1 tens   − 10

    _____ tens   _____

6. Use the number line to subtract. Circle the number that you land on. What is the difference?

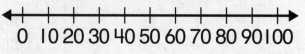

0 10 20 30 40 50 60 70 80 90 100

$80 - 20 =$ _____

GO on

Chapter Test, Form 3B *(continued)*

Write the correct answer.

7. Use related facts to add and subtract.

$20 + \underline{\hspace{1cm}} = 80$

$80 - 20 = \underline{\hspace{1cm}}$

8. Subtract. Write a related addition fact.

$60 - 40 = \underline{\hspace{1cm}}$

$\underline{\hspace{1cm}} + \underline{\hspace{1cm}} = \underline{\hspace{1cm}}$

9. Write the subtraction number sentence. Then write a related addition fact.

Becky saw 50 green beans in her garden. She picked 20 for dinner. How many green beans are still in the garden?

$\underline{\hspace{1cm}} - \underline{\hspace{1cm}} = \underline{\hspace{1cm}}$

$\underline{\hspace{1cm}} + \underline{\hspace{1cm}} = \underline{\hspace{1cm}}$

10. Write the subtraction number sentence. Then write a related addition fact.

In the morning, Carter read 80 pages of his book. In the afternoon, he read 10 more pages. How many more pages did Carter read in the morning?

$\underline{\hspace{1cm}} - \underline{\hspace{1cm}} = \underline{\hspace{1cm}}$

$\underline{\hspace{1cm}} + \underline{\hspace{1cm}} = \underline{\hspace{1cm}}$

STOP

Name ________________________________

Standardized Test Practice

Listen as your teacher reads each problem.
Choose the correct answer.

Example A

5 tens + 1 ten = ______ tens
50 + 10 = ______

○ 5 tens; 50

○ 6 tens; 60

○ 7 tens; 70

○ 8 tens; 80

Example B

Count on to add. What is the sum?

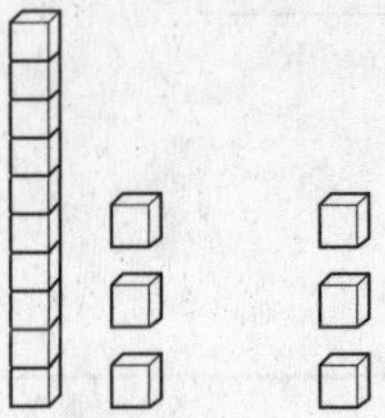

13 + 3 = ______

○ 26 ○ 16

○ 15 ○ 10

1. Add.

	tens	ones
	1	4
+		3

○ 17

○ 20

○ 21

○ 27

2. Write your answer.

17 + 5 = ______

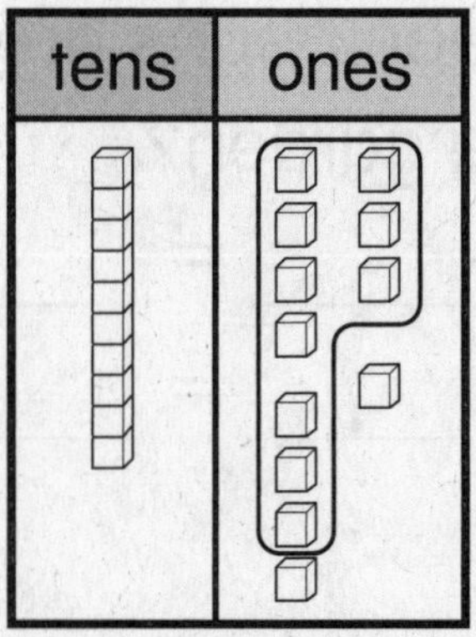

○ 12 ○ 19

○ 22 ○ 32

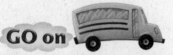

GO on

Standardized Test Practice (continued)

Listen as your teacher reads each problem.
Choose the correct answer.

3. Subtract.

6 tens − 2 tens = _____ tens

60 − 20 = _____

○ 3 tens; 30

○ 4 tens, 40

○ 5 tens, 50

○ 6 tens, 60

4. Subtract.

9 tens	90
− 2 tens	− 20
_____ tens	_____

○ 7 tens, 70

○ 5 tens, 50

○ 2 tens, 20

○ 1 tens, 10

5. Use the number line to subtract. What is the difference?

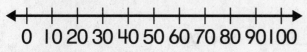

0 10 20 30 40 50 60 70 80 90 100

60 − 20 = _____

○ 10

○ 20

○ 40

○ 50

6. Subtract. What is the related addition fact?

80 − 50 = _____

○ 50 + 20 = 70

○ 20 + 60 = 80

○ 50 + 30 = 80

○ 50 + 40 = 90

STOP

Name _____

 # Oral Assessment

Preparation: Connecting cubes, base-ten blocks, and board access are needed for this assessment.

Directions: This test targets those students who have developing verbal skills—both oral and written. Ask the questions below. Have students record their answers, or record the answers they supply.

1. Write 5 tens + 4 tens = _____ tens on the board. Ask: **What is the sum?**

2. Set 4 base-ten rods and 7 ones cubes in front of the student. Add 3 more ones cubes. Say: **Count on to add 47 + 3. Write the sum.**

3. Draw a tens and ones chart on the board. Write 15 + 4 in the chart. Say: **Add. Write the sum.**

4. Draw a tens and ones chart on a piece of paper. Write 15 + 5 = _____ on the board. Say: **Place the connecting cubes on the tens and ones chart to show how to solve this problem with regrouping.** Draw a picture to show how you got the sum.

5. Write 4 tens − 2 tens = _____ tens   40 − 20 = _____ on the board. Say: **Subtract. Write your answers.**

6. Draw a number line with multiples of 10 from 0 to 50 on the board. Write 50 − 40 = _____ under the number line. Say: **Use the number line to subtract. Circle the number you land on. Write the difference.**

7. Write 10 + _____ = 40 and 40 − 10 = _____. Say: **Use related facts to add and subtract. Write your answers.**

8. Write 80 − 50 = _____ and _____ + _____ = _____. Say: **Subtract. Write a related addition fact.**

Notes

_____

_____

_____

_____

Oral Assessment
Response Sheet

1. _____ 2. _____

3. _____ 4. _____

5. _____ 6. _____

_____

7. _____ 8. _____

_____ _____

Name _____

 # Listening Assessment

Preparation: A large number of connecting cubes and a number line with multiples of 10 to 100 are needed for this assessment.

Directions: Ask students to perform the following tasks.

1. Put 40 cubes in front of you. Take away 20 cubes. Write a subtraction number sentence that shows what you did.

2. Put 27 cubes in front of you. Add 2 cubes. Write an addition number sentence that shows what you did.

3. Use the number line to help you subtract 80 − 20. Write the difference.

4. Use the number line to help you subtract 70 − 40. Write the difference.

5. Use the cubes to show regrouping for 13 + 8. Write the sum.

6. Subtract 90 − 50. What is the difference? Write a related addition fact.

Notes

_____

_____

_____

_____

Name _____

 **Listening Assessment
Response Sheet**

1. _____   2. _____

3. _____   4. _____

5. _____   6. _____

_____

Am I Ready?

Practice

Count. Write the number.

1. _____

2. _____

Count each group of stars. Circle the answer.

3. ★★★★★★★ _____ ★★★★★

   is more than   is fewer than

4. ★★★★ _____ ★★★★★★★★

   is more than   is fewer than

Circle the answer.

5. 9 frogs are in the pond. 5 frogs are on a log.
   Where are there fewer frogs?

   in the pond   on a log

Am I Ready?

Review

Count each group of objects. Circle the answer.
Example:

 _____

is more than   (is fewer than)

1.  _____

is more than   is fewer than

2. 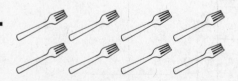 _____

is more than   is fewer than

3.  _____

is more than   is fewer than

Am I Ready?

Apply

The picture graph shows how many of each kind of fish are in the tank.

Fish in the Tank

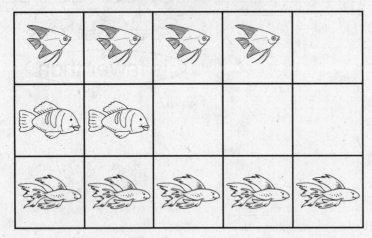

1. How many  are in the 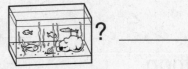 ? _____

2. How many 🐟 are in the 🪟 ? _____

3. How many 🐠 are in the 🪟 ? _____

4. How many fish are in the altogether?

_____

Diagnostic Test

Am I Ready for the Chapter?

Count. Write the number of objects you counted.

1.  🐞 🐞 🐞 🐞 🐞 🐞 _____

2. _____

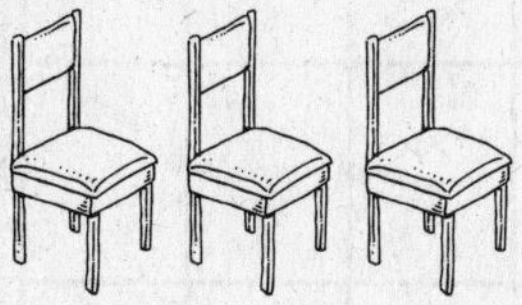

3. _____

4. _____

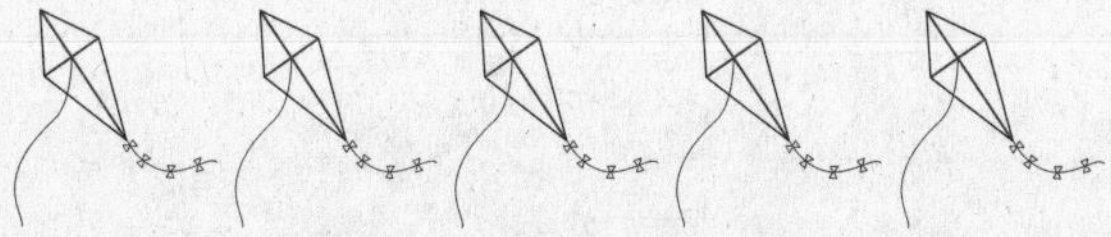

Count each group of triangles. Circle the answer.

5. 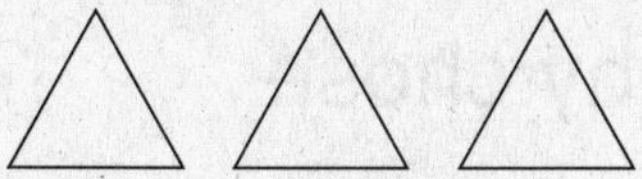 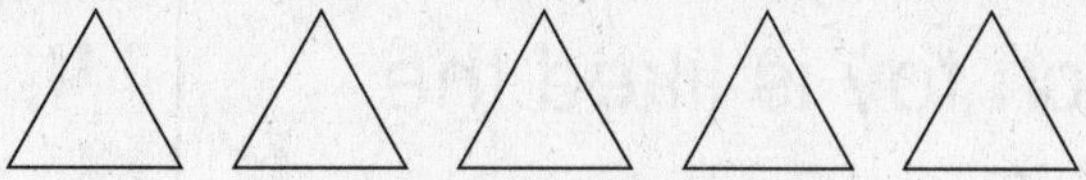 △ △ △   △ △ △ △ △

   is more than   is fewer than

6.   △ △ △   △ △ △
   △ △ △   △ △ △
   △ △ △

   is more than   is fewer than

Circle the answer.

7. 6 cows are in the barn. 4 cows are in the field.
   Which place has more cows?
   the barn   the field

Name _____

Pretest

1. How many students ride the 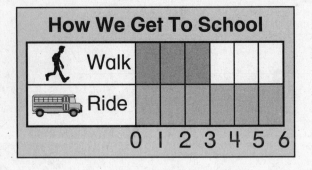 to school?

_____

How We Get To School							
🚶 Walk							
🚌 Ride							
	0	1	2	3	4	5	6

2. How many students chose 🐷? _____

Favorite Animals

Cow	🐄	🐄	🐄	🐄	🐄
Pig	🐖	🐖			
Chicken	🐔	🐔	🐔		

3. Which toy is liked the most? _____

Favorite Toy		
Toy	Tally	Total
✈️ Plane	𝍸𝍸	5
🚗 Car	||||	4
🚂 Train	𝍸𝍸|	6

4. How many chose 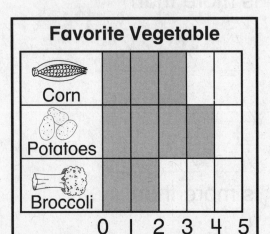?

_____

Favorite Vegetable

🌽 Corn						
🥔 Potatoes						
🥦 Broccoli						
	0	1	2	3	4	5

Name _____

Check My Progress   *(Lessons 1 through 4)*

The students voted for their favorite fruit. Amie made a tally chart to show how the students voted.

Favorite Fruit		
Fruit	Tally	Total
🍇 Grapes	IIII I	5
🍎 Apples	IIII	4
🍊 Oranges	IIII I	6

1. Use the tally chart to make a picture graph.

Favorite Fruit									
🍇 Grapes									
🍎 Apples									
🍊 Oranges									

2. Did more students choose apples or oranges?

_____

3. How many students chose grapes? _____

4. Did fewer students choose grapes or apples?

_____

5. How many more students chose grapes than oranges? _____

6. How many students were surveyed? _____

Name ______________________________

Vocabulary Test

Fill in the blanks. Use the words in the box.

bar graph	tally chart	picture graph	survey

1. A ______________ uses bars to show data.

2. A ____________________ shows data using pictures.

3. You can collect data by taking a __________.

4. A ______________ shows a mark for each vote in a survey.

Draw lines to match.

5. tally chart

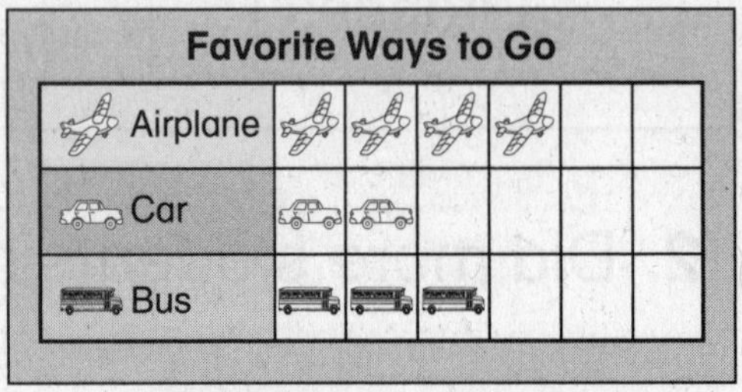

Favorite Ways to Go
Airplane
Car
Bus

6. picture graph

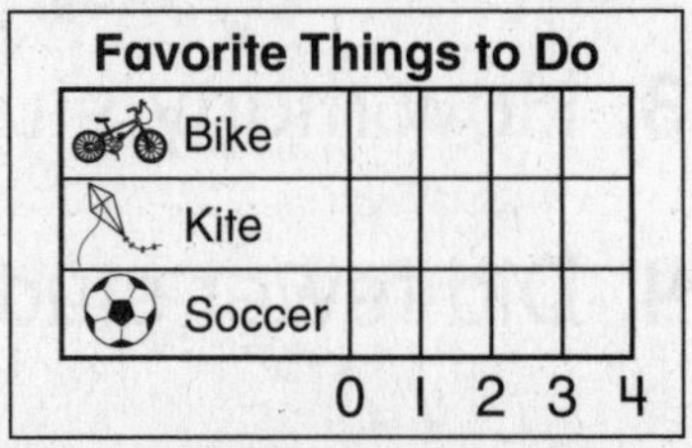

Favorite Things to Do
Bike
Kite
Soccer
0 1 2 3 4

7. bar graph

Favorite Fruit

Fruit	Tally	Total
Banana	卌 |	
Apple	|||	
Pear	||||	

Chapter Test, Form 1A

Read the questions. Circle the correct answer.

1. How many ![elephant]?

Animals in the Zoo

Elephant	🐘	🐘	🐘		
Lion	🦁	🦁			
Monkey	🐒	🐒	🐒	🐒	🐒

A. 2   **B.** 3   **C.** 4

Favorite Fruit		
Fruit	Tally	Total
Banana	⩘I	
Apple	|||	
Pear	||||	

2. How many votes did the get?

F. 4   **G.** 5   **H.** 6

3. Which fruit has the most votes?

A. apple   **B.** banana   **C.** pear   GO on

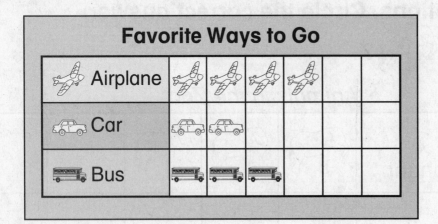

Favorite Ways to Go

Airplane	✈	✈	✈	✈		
Car	🚗	🚗				
Bus	🚌	🚌	🚌			

4. How many ?

A. 4   **B.** 5   **C.** 6

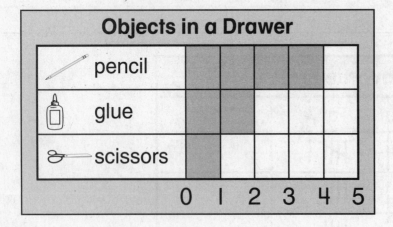

Objects in a Drawer

pencil						
glue						
scissors						
	0	1	2	3	4	5

5. How many more ✏ than 🍶 ?

F. 2   **G.** 3   **H.** 4

STOP

Name _____

Chapter Test, Form 1B

Read the questions. Circle the correct answer.

1. How many 🦃?

Animals on the Farm

Horse	🐎	🐎			
Turkey	🦃	🦃	🦃	🦃	
Sheep	🐑	🐑	🐑		

A. 2   **B.** 3   **C.** 4

Number of Tools		
Tool	Tally	Total
Pail	ⅢⅠ	
Shovel	‖	
Rake	‖‖	

2. How many 🪣?

F. 4   **G.** 5   **H.** 6

3. Which item has the most votes?

A. rake   **B.** shovel   **C.** pail

GO on

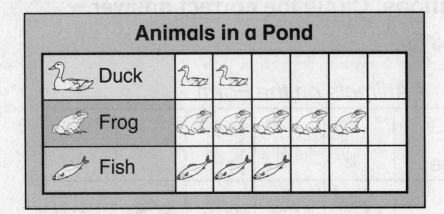

Animals in a Pond

Duck						
Frog						
Fish						

4. How many  ?

A. 2   **B.** 3   **C.** 4

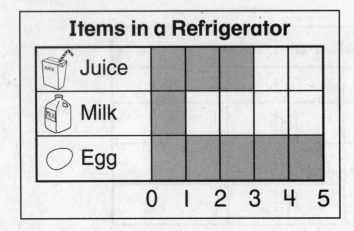

Items in a Refrigerator

Juice					
Milk					
Egg					
0 1 2 3 4 5					

5. How many more ◯ than ▭ ?

F. 2   **G.** 3   **H.** 4

STOP

Name ______________________________

Chapter Test, Form 2A

Read the questions. Circle the correct answer.

Favorite Foods		
Food	Tally	Total
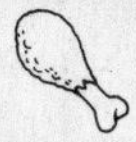 Chicken	IIII	
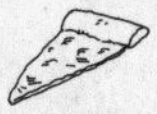 Pizza	~~IIII~~ II	
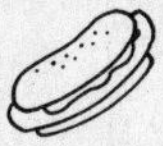 Hot Dog	~~IIII~~ I	

1. How many students voted for 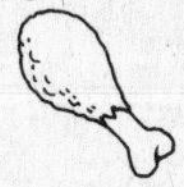 ?

A. 3 **B.** 4

C. 5 **D.** 6

2. How many more students voted for 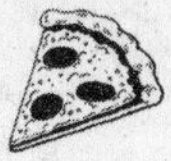 than 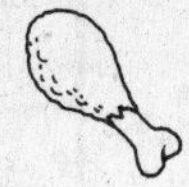 ?

F. 6 **G.** 5

H. 4 **I.** 3

3. How many fewer students voted for 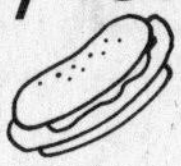 than 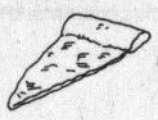 ?

A. 1 **B.** 2

C. 3 **D.** 4

4. How many students voted altogether?

F. 16 **G.** 18

H. 17 **I.** 19

GO on 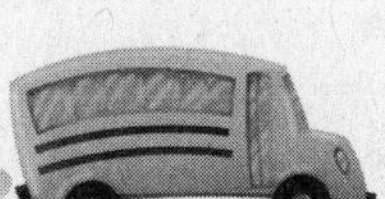

Chapter Test, Form 2A   (continued)

Bugs in the Garden		
Bug	Tally	Total
🐞 Ladybug	卌	
🦗 Cricket	||	
🐜 Ant	卌 ||	

5. Look at the tally chart. Color in the bar graph to show how many of each bug.

Bugs in the Garden								
🐞 Ladybug								
🦗 Cricket								
🐜 Ant								
	0	1	2	3	4	5	6	7

6. Write how many.

_____   _____   _____

7. How many more 🐜 are in the garden than 🐞? _____

Chapter Test, Form 2B

Read the questions. Circle the correct answer.

Favorite Pets		
Pet	Tally	Total
 🐱 Cat	IIII I	
 🐕 Dog	IIII	
 🦜 Bird	III	

1. How many students chose 🦜?

A. 2   **B.** 3

C. 4   **D.** 5

2. How many students chose 🐱?

F. 3   **G.** 4

H. 5   **I.** 6

3. How many fewer students chose 🐕 than 🐱?

A. 1   **B.** 2

C. 3   **D.** 4

4. How many students were surveyed?

F. 10   **G.** 11

H. 12   **I.** 13

GO on

Chapter Test, Form 2B (continued)

Clothes in a Closet		
Clothes	Tally	Total
Pants	$\|\|$	
Shirt	$\cancel{\|\|\|\|}$	
Jacket	$\cancel{\|\|\|\|}\ \|$	

5. Look at the tally chart. Color in the bar graph to show how many of each kind of clothes.

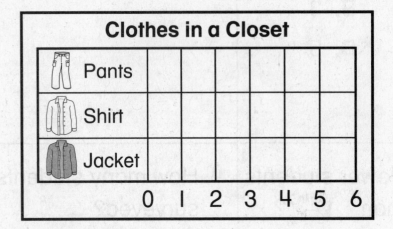

Clothes in a Closet

Pants

Shirt

Jacket

0 1 2 3 4 5 6

6. Write how many.

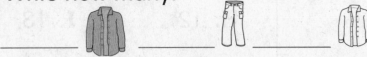

_____ _____ _____

7. How many more in the closet than

 ? _____

STOP

Chapter Test, Form 3A

Use the tally chart to answer the questions.

Favorite Place		
Place	Tally	Total
Circus	ЖΙΙ	
Zoo	ЖΙΙ ΙΙΙ	
Playground	ЖΙΙ Ι	

1. How many people chose the circus? _____ people

2. How many more people chose the zoo than the playground? _____ people

3. How many people took the survey? _____ people

4. Use the tally chart to make a bar graph. Color in the bar graph to show how many voted for each place.

Favorite Place										
Circus										
Zoo										
Playground										

0 1 2 3 4 5 6 7 8 9

5. Which place got the most votes?

_____

GO on

Chapter Test, Form 3A   *(continued)*

6. Complete the graph.

Min likes  and ⚽. Ben likes 🚲.

Jade likes 🪁. Ella likes 🚲 and ⚽.

Favorite Things to Do

🚲 Bike				
🪁 Kite				
⚽ Soccer				

0 1 2 3 4

7. How many students voted? _____

8. Which got the most votes? _____

9. Which got the fewest votes?

_____

10. How many fewer votes did 🪁 get

than 🚲? _____

Chapter Test, Form 3B

Use the tally chart to answer the questions.

Favorite Drink		
Drink	Tally	Total
Milk	卌 I	
Water	IIII	
Juice	卌 II	

1. How many people chose milk? _____ people

2. How many more people chose juice than water?
_____ people

3. How many people took the survey? _____ people

4. Use the tally chart to make a bar graph. Color in the bar graph to show how many voted for each drink.

Favorite Drink

Milk								
Water								
Juice								

0 1 2 3 4 5 6 7

5. Which drink got the most votes?

_____

GO on

Chapter Test, Form 3B (continued)

6. Complete the graph.

Min used a ⚒ and a 🪛. Ben

used a ⚒ and a 🔧. Jade used a 🔧. Ella

used a ⚒ and a 🪛.

Tools Used by Students						
🪛 Screwdriver						
⚒ Hammer						
🔧 Wrench						
	0	1	2	3	4	

7. How many students voted? _____

8. Which got the most votes? _____

9. Which two got the same number of votes?

_____   _____

10. How many more votes did ⚒ get

than 🔧 ? _____

Name _____

Standardized Test Practice

Read the questions. Choose the correct answer.

Example A

Favorite Shape		
Shape	Tally	Total
◯ Circle	ⅲⅰⅰ	
★ Star	ⅲ	
△ Triangle	ⅲⅰ	

Look at the tally chart. How many people voted for the △?

◯ 7   ◯ 6

◯ 5   ◯ 4

1. Use the tally chart to make a picture graph.

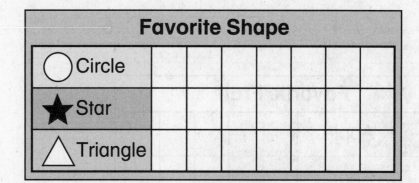

2. How many students voted for ★?

◯ 3   ◯ 4   ◯ 5   ◯ 6

3. How many more students voted for ◯ than ★?

◯ 1   ◯ 2   ◯ 3   ◯ 4

4. Which shape got the most votes?

◯ ★   ◯ □   ◯ ◯   ◯ △

Standardized Test Practice *(continued)*

Animals at the Zoo		
Animal	Tally	Total
🐆 Leopard	||||	
🦭 Seal	卌 ||	
🐘 Elephant	卌	

5. How many 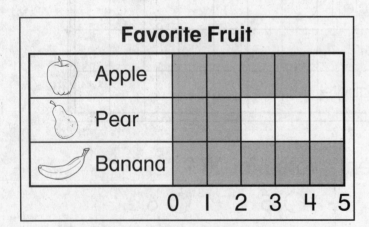 are there?

    ⬭ 5   ⬭ 6   ⬭ 7   ⬭ 8

6. How many fewer votes does 🐆 have than 🦭?

    ⬭ 3   ⬭ 4   ⬭ 5   ⬭ 6

Favorite Fruit						
🍎 Apple						
🍐 Pear						
🍌 Banana						
	0	1	2	3	4	5

7. How many more voted for 🍎 than 🍐?

    ⬭ 1   ⬭ 2   ⬭ 3   ⬭ 4

8. How many total voted for 🍐 and 🍌?

    ⬭ 5   ⬭ 6   ⬭ 7   ⬭ 8

Oral Assessment

Directions: This test targets those students who have developing verbal skills—both oral and written. Ask the questions below and have students record their answers, or record the answers they supply.

1. Show the bar graph to the student. Ask: *How many students chose a dog as their favorite pet?*

2. Show the bar graph to the student. Ask: *How many students chose a cat as their favorite pet?*

3. Using the bar graph again, ask: *How many more students chose dogs than birds?*

4. Show the tally chart to the student. Ask: *How many fewer students chose sea horses than whales?*

Notes

_____

_____

_____

_____

_____

Oral Assessment Response Sheet

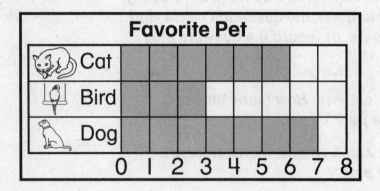

Favorite Pet

	0	1	2	3	4	5	6	7	8
Cat									
Bird									
Dog									

1. _____

2. _____

3. _____

4. _____

Favorite Ocean Animal		
Animal	Tally	Total
Whale	卌 I	6
Dolphin	卌 III	8
Sea Horse	III	3

Name _____

Listening Assessment

1. Draw three circles.
   Draw two squares.
   Draw four stars.
   Draw one triangle.
   Now make a picture graph to show how many
   of each shape.

2. Draw three forks.
   Draw one knife.
   Draw four spoons.
   Now shade the bar graph to show how many
   of each.

3. Draw seven paper clips.
   Draw four pencils.
   Draw five books.
   Make a tally chart with the objects.

Notes

_____

_____

_____

_____

_____

 # Listening Assessment Response Sheet

I.

Shapes					
◯ Circle					
☐ Square					
△ Triangle					

2.

Silverware					
Spoon					
Fork					
Knife					
0	1	2	3	4	5

3.

Objects on a Desk		
Object	Tally	Total
Paper Clip		
Pencil		
Book		

Am I Ready?

Practice

Circle the object that is longer.

1.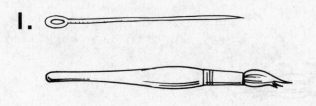

2.

3. Look at the pencil sharpener. Draw an object that is longer.

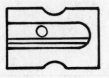

4. Write the number that comes next.

11, 12, 13, 14, 15, _____

5. I come after 15. I come before 17. What number am I?

_____

Am I Ready?

Review

Circle the object that is longer.

1.

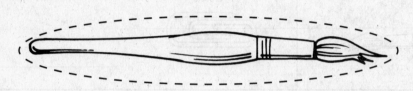

2.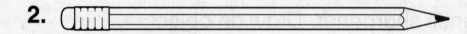

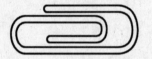

3.

4.

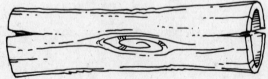

Grade 1 • Chapter 8 Measurement and Time

Am I Ready?

Apply

1. Draw an object that is longer than the pencil sharpener and shorter than the paintbrush.

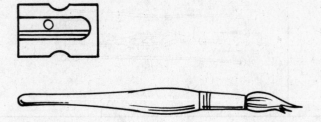

2. Draw an object that is longer than the paper clip and shorter than the pencil.

3. Draw an object that is longer than the key and shorter than the knife.

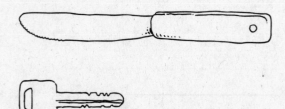

Diagnostic Test

Am I Ready for the Chapter?

Circle the object that is longer.

I.

2.

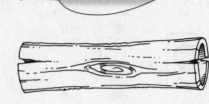

---

3. Look at the marker. Draw an object that is shorter.

4. Write the number that comes next.

10, 9, 8, 7, _____

5. I come after 18. I come before 20. What number am I?

_____

Name _____

Pretest

Read the directions. Circle the correct answer.

1. Circle the object that is longer.

2. Circle the object that is shorter.

3. Write 1 for long, 2 for longer, 3 for longest.

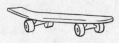 _____

 _____

 _____

4. What time is it?

F. half past 3

G. half past 4

H. 5 o'clock

Name _____

Check My Progress   *(Lessons 1 through 4)*

1. Order the objects by length. Write 1 for short,
2 for shorter, and 3 for shortest.

   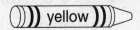   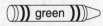

_____   _____   _____

Compare. Circle the longer object.

2.

3.

Measure using . Write how many.

4.  about _____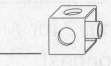

Compare the object. Circle the correct choice.

5. The desk is longer than the book. The book
is longer than the pencil. Is the pencil longer
than or shorter than the desk?

longer than   shorter than

6. The juice box is shorter than the lunch tray.
The lunch tray is shorter than the table. Is the
table longer than or shorter than the juice box?

longer than   shorter than

Grade 1 • Chapter 8 Measurement and Time

Vocabulary Test

Choose a word from the box to complete each sentence.

analog clock	digital clock	length
measure	unit	

I. These objects are in order by

_____.

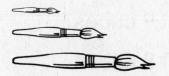

2. An object used to measure is a

_____.

3. To find the length of a pencil, I can

_____ it.

4. A clock that has an hour hand and a minute

hand is an _____.

5. A clock that uses only numbers to show

time is a _____.

Name _____

Chapter Test, Form 1A

Read each question carefully. Circle the correct answer.

1. Which is the longest pencil?

A.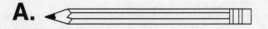

B.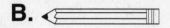

C.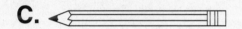

2. About how many cubes long is this marker?

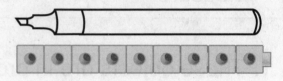

F. about 4 cubes

G. about 9 cubes

H. about 8 cubes

---

3. Circle the time.

A. 11 o'clock

B. half past 12:00

C. 1 o'clock

4. Circle the time.

F. half past 5

G. 6 o'clock

H. half past 6

GO on

Chapter Test, Form 1A   (continued)

5. About how many cubes long is this turtle?

A. about 6 cubes

B. about 5 cubes

C. about 4 cubes

6. Which animal is the longest?

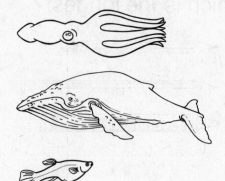

F. fish

G. squid

H. whale

7. What time is it?

A. 9 o'clock

B. half past 9

C. half past 10

8. What time is it?

F. half past 1

G. 2 o'clock

H. half past 2

STOP

Name _____

Chapter Test, Form 1B

Read each question carefully. Circle the correct answer.

1. Which is the longest?

A.

B. _pencil_

C. _yellow crayon_

2. About how many cubes long is the bread?

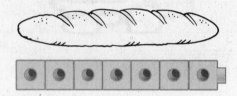

A. about 5 cubes

B. about 6 cubes

C. about 7 cubes

3. Circle the time.

F. 3 o'clock

G. half past 3

H. 4 o'clock

4. Circle the time.

3:30

F. half past 2

G. half past 3

H. half past 4

GO on

194

Grade 1 • Chapter 8 Measurement and Time

Chapter Test, Form 1B *(continued)*

5. About how many cubes long is this trumpet?

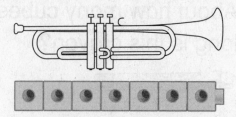

A. about 5 cubes

B. about 6 cubes

C. about 7 cubes

6. Which fruit is the shortest?

F. watermelon

G. banana

H. apple

7. What time is it?

A. 10 o'clock

B. half past 11

C. 12 o'clock

8. What time is it?

7:00

F. 7 o'clock

G. half past 7

H. 8 o'clock

Chapter Test, Form 2A

Circle the correct answer.

1. Which is the longest paintbrush?

A.

B.

C.

D.

2. About how many cubes long is this crayon?

F. about 9 cubes

G. about 7 cubes

H. about 6 cubes

I. about 5 cubes

3. Circle the time.

A. 6 o'clock
B. 7 o'clock
C. half past 7
D. 8 o'clock

4. Circle the time.

F. half past 5
G. half past 6
H. 7 o'clock
I. half past 8

GO on

Chapter Test, Form 2A   (continued)

Read each question carefully. Write the correct answer.

5. Is the 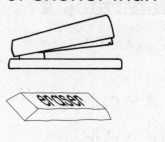 longer than or shorter than the 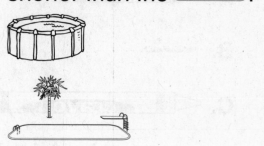?

_____

6. Is the longer than or shorter than the ?

_____

7. About how many cubes long is this horn?

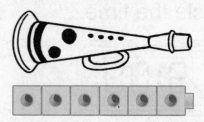

about _____ cubes

8. Write 1 for long, 2 for longer, 3 for longest.

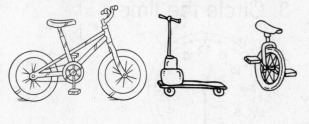

_____   _____   _____

Write the time.

9.

half past _____

10. 5 o'clock

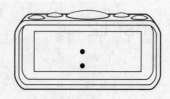

STOP

Chapter Test, Form 2B

Circle the correct answer.

1. Which is the shortest crayon?

A.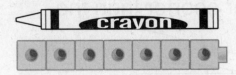

B. ◁ crayon

C. ◁ crayon

D. ◁ crayon

2. About how many cubes long is this crayon?

F. about 9 cubes

G. about 8 cubes

H. about 7 cubes

I. about 6 cubes

3. Circle the time.

A. half past 10

B. 11 o'clock

C. half past 11

D. half past 12

4. Circle the time.

9:00

F. half past 8

G. 9 o'clock

H. half past 9

I. 10 o'clock

GO on

Chapter Test, Form 2B   (continued)

Read each question carefully. Write the correct answer.

5. Is the  longer than or shorter than the ?

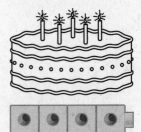

_____

6. Is the  longer than or shorter than the ?

_____

7. About how many cubes long is this birthday cake?

about _____ cubes

8. Write 1 for long, 2 for longer, 3 for longest.

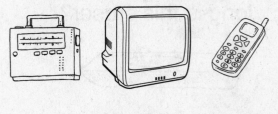

_____   _____   _____

Write the time.

9.

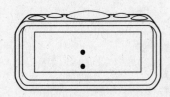

half past _____

10. half past 6

Name _____

Chapter Test, Form 3A

Write the correct answer.

1. Circle the string that is the longest.

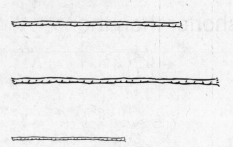

2. Circle the key that is the shortest.

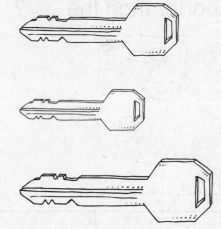

3. About how many cubes long is this eraser?

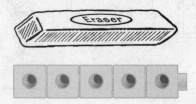

about _____ cubes

4. Write the time on the digital clock.

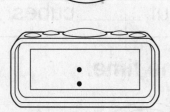

GO on

Chapter Test, Form 3A   *(continued)*

Read each question carefully. Write the correct answer.

5. Is the  longer than or shorter than the ?

_____

6. Is the longer than or shorter than the ?

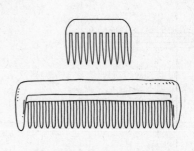

_____

7. About how many cubes long is this hand soap?

about _____ cubes

8. Write 1 for long, 2 for longer, 3 for longest.

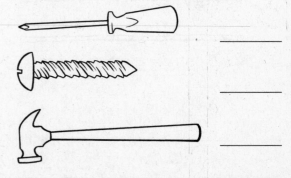

_____

_____

_____

Write the time.

9.

_____ o'clock

10. half past 2

Chapter Test, Form 3B

Write the correct answer.

1. Circle the pencil that is longer.

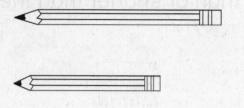

3. About how many cubes long is this crayon?

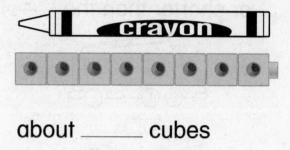

about _____ cubes

2. Circle the string that is the shortest.

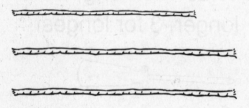

4. Write the time on the digital clock.

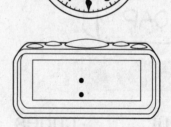

GO on

Chapter Test, Form 3B *(continued)*

Read each question carefully. Write the correct answer.

5. Is the  longer than or shorter than the _____?

_____

6. Is the  longer than or shorter than the _____?

_____

7. About how many cubes long is this football?

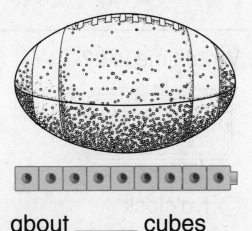

about _____ cubes

8. Write 1 for long, 2 for longer, 3 for longest.

_____

_____

_____

Write the time.

9.

half past _____

10. 3 o'clock.

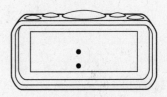

Name _____

Standardized Test Practice

Listen as your teacher reads each problem.
Choose the correct answer.

Example A

Which ribbon is the longest?

Example B

Which toy is the shortest?

1. What time is it?

○ 10 o'clock

○ half past 10

○ 11 o'clock

2. What time is it?

○ 1 o'clock

○ half past 1

○ 2 o'clock

GO on

Name _____

Standardized Test Practice   (continued)

Listen as your teacher reads each problem. Choose the correct answer.

3. About how many cubes long is the pencil?

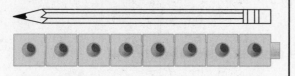

○ about 7 cubes

○ about 8 cubes

○ about 9 cubes

4. Which fish is the shortest?

○

○

○

5. What time is it?

○ 6 o'clock

○ 7 o'clock

○ half past 7

6. What time is it?

○ half past 9

○ 9 o'clock

○ half past 8

STOP

Name _____

 # Oral Assessment

Preparation: A set of connecting cubes and a clock are needed for this assessment. You will also need the following classroom objects: a 6-inch piece of string or yarn, a pencil, and a paper clip.

Directions: This test targets those students who may have developing verbal skills—both oral and written. Ask the questions below and have students record their answers, or record the answers they supply.

1. Show the 6-inch piece of yarn/string to the student. Ask: *About how many cubes long is this string?*

2. Ask: *Which is longer, the pencil or the paper clip?*

3. Show 1:00 on the analog clock. Ask: *What time is it?*

4. Ask: *How do you show half past 1 on the analog clock?*

5. Draw a digital clock. Ask: *How do you show 2:00 on a digital clock?*

6. Draw a digital clock. Say: *How do you show half past 2 on a digital clock?*

Notes

_____

_____

_____

_____

_____

_____

**Oral Assessment
Response Sheet**

1. _____ **2.** _____

3. _____ o'clock **4.**

5. 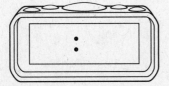 **6.**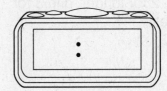

Listening Assessment

Directions: Ask students to complete each of the following groups of tasks.

Preparation: A set of connecting cubes, index cards, and several classroom objects (e.g., staplers, pencils, markers, pencil cases, crayons, paper, chalk, erasers, etc.) are needed for this assessment.

1. Use a ruler to draw a line. Measure the length of the line using cubes. Write how long the line is.

2. Choose two objects in the classroom. Write a sentence about the two objects using the words *shorter than* or *longer than*.

3. Draw a paintbrush. Use cubes to measure the paintbrush. Write about how long the paintbrush is.

4. Draw a football. Draw a baseball bat. Circle the picture that is longer. Draw an X on the one that is shorter.

5. Draw 3 objects. Write 1 for long, 2 for longer, and 3 for longest.

Notes

_____

_____

_____

_____

_____

_____

Name _____

Listening Assessment
Response Sheet

1. Draw your line here.

about _____ cubes

2. Write your answer here.

_____

_____

3. _____

about _____ cubes

4. _____

5. _____

Name _____

Am I Ready?

Practice

Draw a line to match the objects that are the same shape.

1.

2.

3.

---

4. Andy enjoys sailing. What shape is this sail? Circle the name.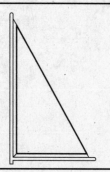

     triangle   square   rectangle

---

5. Circle the shape that shows 4 equal parts. Put a X on the shape that shows 3 equal parts.

  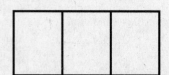

Am I Ready?

Review

Draw a line to match the objects that are the same shape.

1.

2.

3.

4.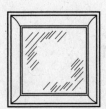

---

5. Color the shape that shows 4 equal parts blue.

  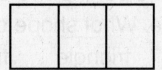

Name _____

Am I Ready?

Apply

Circle the word that is the correct answer.

1. Emma saw a traffic sign that looked like this. What shape is it?

    square   triangle   trapezoid

2. Mr. Morris asked each student to find an object that looks like a geometric shape. Eric drew a wheel. What shape is it?

    rectangle   circle   triangle

3. Maria drew a shape with curves but no sides and no vertices. What shape did Maria draw?

    square   circle   trapezoid

4. Keenan drew a shape with three sides. What shape did Keenan draw?

    rectangle   square   triangle

5. Liz wanted to make a new shape using two squares. She put the two squares together side by side. What shape did Liz make?

    rectangle   triangle   trapezoid

Diagnostic Test

Am I Ready for the Chapter?

Draw a line to match the objects that are the same shape.

1.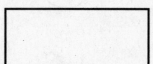

2.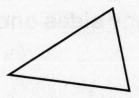

3.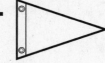

---

4. Megan sent this postcard to her aunt. What shape is it? Circle the name.

   triangle   square   rectangle

---

5. Circle the shape that shows 3 equal parts. Underline the shape that shows 2 equal parts.

 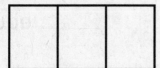

Name _____

Pretest

Write the correct answer.

1. Circle the square.

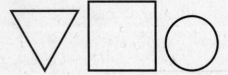

2. Circle the triangle.

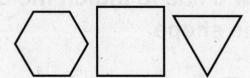

Write how many sides and vertices.

3.

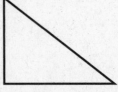

_____ sides

_____ vertices

4.

_____ sides

_____ vertices

5. Write how many equal parts.

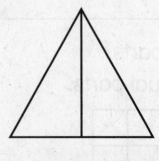

_____ equal parts

6. Write how many equal parts.

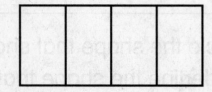

_____ equal parts

Grade 1 · Chapter 9 Two-Dimensional Shapes and Equal Shares

Name _____

Check My Progress *(Lessons I through 4)*

Color the shapes that match the rule.

I. 4 sides

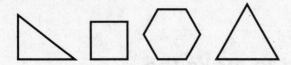

2. 0 vertices

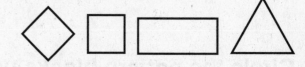

3. 3 sides

4. squares

Write how many.

5.

_____ sides

_____ vertices

6.

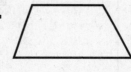

_____ sides

_____ vertices

7.

_____ sides

_____ vertices

8.

_____ sides

_____ vertices

9. Kaylee has a shape with 3 sides and 3 vertices.
Brayden has a shape with 4 sides of equal
length and 4 vertices. Name the two shapes.
Kaylee has a _____. Brayden has a

_____.

Check My Progress *(Lessons 5 through 7)*

Color all the closed shapes.

1.

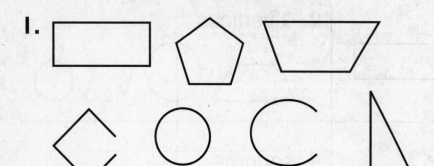

Circle the pattern blocks used to make the shape.

2.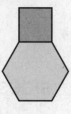

3.

4.

Name _____

Vocabulary Test

Match the two-dimensional shape to its name.

1. square

2. circle

3. rectangle

4. triangle

5. trapezoid

Choose a word from the box to complete each sentence.

composite shape	equal parts	two-dimensional shape	whole

6. The entire amount or all of the parts is the

   _____.

7. Two or more shapes that are put together make
   a new shape are called a _____.

8. Parts of a whole that have the same size are
   called _____.

9. A flat shape, such as a circle, a triangle, or a
   square is a _____.

Chapter Test, Form 1A

Circle the correct answer.

1. Which shape is a rectangle?

A.

B.

C.

2. How many sides does this shape have?

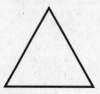

F. 2

G. 3

H. 4

3. Which shape is a trapezoid?

A.

B.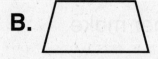

C.

4. What is the name of this shape?

F. rectangle

G. square

H. circle

GO on

Chapter Test, Form 1A (continued)

5. Tina made a new shape by putting 3 triangles together. What shape did she make?

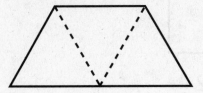

  A. rectangle

  B. trapezoid

  C. circle

6. What two shapes were used to make this rectangle?

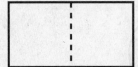

  F. two triangles

  G. two squares

  H. two trapezoids

7. Which shape has 3 sides and 3 vertices?

  A.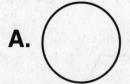

  B.

  C.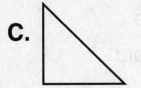

8. How many equal parts make up the whole?

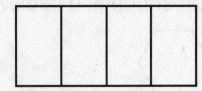

  F. 4

  G. 3

  H. 2

STOP

Chapter Test, Form IB

Circle the correct answer.

1. Which shape is a triangle?

A.

B.

C.

2. How many sides does this shape have?

F. 2

G. 3

H. 4

3. Which shape is a circle?

A.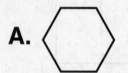

B.

C.

4. What is the name of this shape?

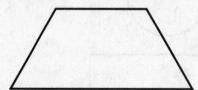

F. square

G. triangle

H. trapezoid

GO on

Chapter Test, Form 1B *(continued)*

5. Max wanted to make a new shape by putting two squares together. What shape did he make?

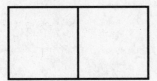

A. trapezoid

B. triangle

C. rectangle

6. What two shapes were used to make this shape?

F. two triangles

G. two circles

H. two hexagons

7. Which shape has 0 sides and 0 vertices?

A.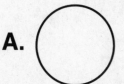

B.

C.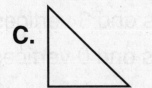

8. How many equal parts make up the whole?

F. 2

G. 3

H. 4

Name _____

Chapter Test, Form 2A

Circle the correct answer.

1. What is the name of this shape?

   A. rectangle

   B. trapezoid

   C. triangle

   D. square

2. How many sides does this shape have?

   F. 0

   G. 2

   H. 4

   I. 6

3. How many sides and vertices does the square have?

   A. 3 sides and 3 vertices

   B. 3 sides and 4 vertices

   C. 4 sides and 4 vertices

   D. 0 sides and 0 vertices

4. How many sides and vertices does a circle have?

   F. 2 sides and 2 vertices

   G. 4 sides and 4 vertices

   H. 3 sides and 3 vertices

   I. 0 sides and 0 vertices

GO on

Grade 1 · Chapter 9 Two-Dimensional Shapes and Equal Shares

Chapter Test, Form 2A   (continued)

Circle the correct answer.

5. What two shapes were
used to make this
rectangle?

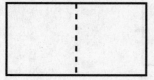

two trapezoids

two squares

6. Carlos put together the
three shapes shown.
Circle the new shape he
made.

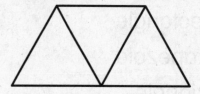

trapezoid

circle

---

7. Which shape shows
2 equal parts?

A.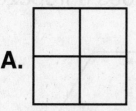

B.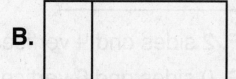

C.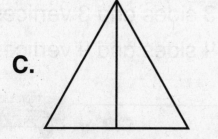

8. How many parts are
shaded?

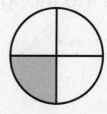

_____ of _____ parts

Name _____

Chapter Test, Form 2B

Circle the correct answer.

I. What shape is this?

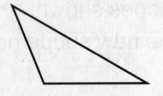

   A. rectangle

   B. trapezoid

   C. triangle

   D. square

2. How many sides does this shape have?

   F. 0

   G. 4

   H. 5

   I. 6

3. How many sides and vertices does the triangle have?

   A. 3 sides and 2 vertices

   B. 3 sides and 3 vertices

   C. 4 sides and 4 vertices

   D. 2 sides and 3 vertices

4. How many sides and vertices does a trapezoid have?

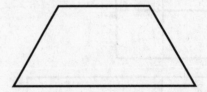

   F. 2 sides and 4 vertices

   G. 0 sides and 0 vertices

   H. 3 sides and 3 vertices

   I. 4 sides and 4 vertices

GO on

Chapter Test, Form 2B *(continued)*

Circle the correct answer.

5. What two shapes were used to make this square?

two triangles

two rectangles

6. Hannah joined two shapes. She made the following shape. What two shapes did Hannah join together?

two trapezoids

two triangles

7. Draw lines to show 4 equal parts.

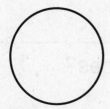

8. Write how many parts are shaded.

_____ of _____ parts

Name _____

Chapter Test, Form 3A

1. Circle the name of this shape.

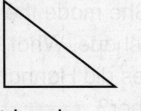

triangle   square

2. How many sides and vertices does this shape have?

____ sides ____ vertices

---

3. Write how many sides and vertices the circle has.

____ sides ____ vertices

4. Circle the two-dimensional shape this object looks like?

trapezoid   rectangle

---

5. Which shape below has 3 sides and 3 vertices? Circle the name.

      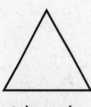   

square   triangle   circle

GO on

Chapter Test, Form 3A (continued)

Circle the correct answer.

6. Abbi made a new shape by putting three triangles together. What shape did she make?

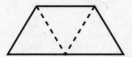

trapezoid

triangle

7. Carol made a new shape. What shapes did Carol use to make the new shape?

triangles

circles

8. Brandon saw a shape with 3 sides and 3 vertices. Did Brandon see a circle, a triangle, or a square?

_____

9. Donna drew a shape with 0 sides and 0 vertices. Did Dona draw a circle, a triangle, or a square?

_____

10. Circle the pattern blocks used to make the shape.

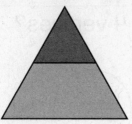

11. Draw lines to show 4 equal parts.

Chapter Test, Form 3B

1. Circle the name of this shape.

square   rectangle

2. How many sides and vertices does this shape have?

____ sides
____ vertices

3. Write how many sides and vertices.

____ sides ____ vertices

4. Circle the two-dimensional shape this object looks like.

circle   trapezoid

5. Which shape below has 4 sides and 4 vertices? Circle the name.

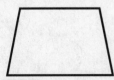

trapezoid   triangle   circle

GO on

Chapter Test, Form 3B   *(continued)*

Circle the correct answer.

6. Jaden made a new shape by putting 2 triangles together. What new shape did Jaden make?

square   rectangle

7. Adam made a new shape. What shapes did he use to make the shape?

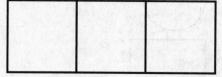

rectangles   squares

8. Tamika saw a shape with 4 sides and 4 vertices. Did she see a circle, a triangle, or a square?

_____

9. Guy drew a shape with 3 sides and 3 vertices. Did he draw a circle, a triangle, or a square?

_____

10. Circle the pattern blocks used to make the shape.

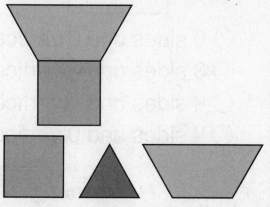

11. Draw lines to show 2 equal parts.

Name _____

Standardized Test Practice

Listen as your teacher reads each problem.
Choose the correct answer.

Example A

Which shape is a square?

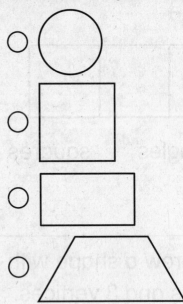

Example B

Which shape is a trapezoid?

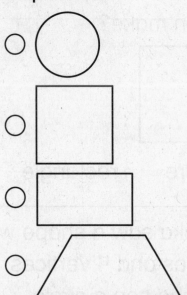

1. How many sides and vertices does a circle have?

○ 0 sides and 0 vertices
○ 3 sides and 3 vertices
○ 4 sides and 4 vertices
○ 4 sides and 2 vertices

2. How many sides and vertices does a rectangle have?

○ 0 sides and 0 vertices
○ 3 sides and 3 vertices
○ 4 sides and 4 vertices
○ 4 sides and 0 vertices

GO on

Standardized Test Practice   (continued)

**Listen as your teacher reads each problem.
Choose the correct answer.**

3. Which pattern block was used to make the shape.

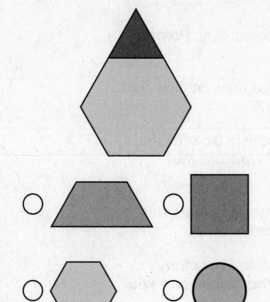

○    ○ ▨

○ ⬡   ○ ⬤

4. How many equal parts make up the whole?

○ 6
○ 4
○ 3
○ 2

5. How many sides and vertices?

△

○ 2 sides and 2 vertices
○ 3 sides and 3 vertices
○ 4 sides and 2 vertices
○ 4 sides and 4 vertices

6. What shapes were used to make this rectangle?

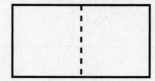

○ squares
○ rectangles
○ triangles
○ trapezoids

Name _____

 **Oral Assessment**

Preparation: Board access and pattern blocks are needed for this assessment.

Directions: This test targets those students who have developing verbal skills—both oral and written. Ask the questions below and have students record their answers, or record the answers they supply.

1. Draw a circle, a square, and a triangle on the board. Say: ***Point to the triangle***.

2. Point to the same circle, square, and triangle you drew on the board. Ask: ***Which shapes have sides and vertices?***

3. Place a rectangle pattern block and a square pattern block on the desk. Ask: ***How are these two shapes alike? How are they different?***

4. Draw a trapezoid on the board. Ask: ***How many sides does this shape have? What is the name of this shape?***

5. Place two triangle pattern blocks on the desk. Ask: ***How many sides and vertices does a triangle have? What shape can you make by putting two triangles together?***

6. Place a hexagon pattern block on the desk. Ask: ***How many triangles does it take to make this shape?***

7. Draw a square on the board. Say: ***Divide the square into 2 equal parts***.

Notes

_____

_____

_____

_____

_____

_____

Oral Assessment
Response Sheet

1. _____

2. _____

3. Alike: _____

Different: _____

4. _____

5. _____

6. _____

7.

Name _____

 # Listening Assessment

Directions: Ask students to perform the following tasks.

Preparation: Writing paper (or response sheet), pencil, and pattern blocks are needed for this assessment.

1. Draw a triangle. Say: *Write how many sides and vertices the triangle has.*

2. Draw a square. Say: *Write how many sides and vertices the square has.*

3. Draw a circle. Ask: *How is the circle different from the triangle and the square?* Write your answer.

4. Draw a rectangle and a square. Ask: *How are these shapes alike? How are they different?* Write your answer.

5. Draw a trapezoid. *Write how many sides and vertices the trapezoid has.*

6. Find two or more pattern blocks of the same shape (such as three triangles or two trapezoids). Ask: *What composite shape can you make by putting the shapes together?* Draw your answer.

7. Say: *Look around the classroom, playground, or your house. See if you can find objects that look like two-dimensional shapes, such as a clock (circle) or a piece of paper (rectangle). Write or draw what you find.*

Notes

_____

_____

_____

_____

_____

_____

_____

Name _____

 **Listening Assessment
Response Sheet**

1. _____ sides
 _____ vertices

2. _____ sides
 _____ vertices

3. _____

4. Alike: _____

 Different: _____

5. _____

6.

7.

Am I Ready?

Practice

Draw an X over the object that is a different shape.

1.

2.   (cube with numbers 1, 2, 3)

Draw a line to match objects that are the same shape.

3.   (button)

4.

5.

6. Anya's fish live in this aquarium.
   What shape is the aquarium? Circle the word.

   sphere   rectangular prism   square

Am I Ready?

Review

Draw a line to match the objects that are the same shape.

I.

2.

3.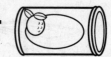

4.

---

5. Allen's new shoes came in this box. What shape is the box? Circle the word.

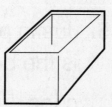

rectangular prism   cube   triangle

Name _____

Am I Ready?

Apply

Solve.

1. Tina won a ball at the carnival. What shape is it?

    cone   circle   sphere

2. Steve drew a shape with 6 faces and 8 vertices. What shape is it?

    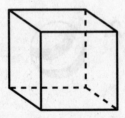

    cube   circle   sphere

3. Mario's fish live in an aquarium. What shape is the aquarium?

    circle   sphere   rectangular prism

4. Maria made orange juice for breakfast. What shape is the container of juice?

    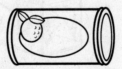

    cylinder   circle   sphere

5. Justin puts his toys in this box. What shape is the box? Circle the word.

    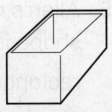

    cube   rectangular prism   triangle

Name _____

Diagnostic Test

Am I Ready for the Chapter?

Draw an X over the object that is a different shape.

1.

2.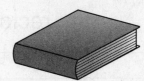

Draw a line to match the objects that are the same shape.

3.

4.

5.

Solve.

6. Hannah's sister was playing with this block. What shape is it? Circle the word.

   square   cube   cone

Pretest

Identify each shape. Circle the name.
Write the number of faces and vertices.

1.    cone   cylinder

_____ faces _____ vertices

2. 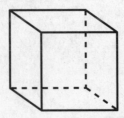   cube   rectangular prism

_____ faces _____ vertices

Circle the shapes used to make each composite shape.

3.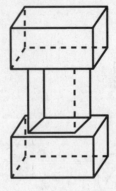

4.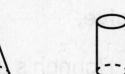

Check My Progress (Lessons 1 through 2)

Color all the shapes that match the name.

1. cylinder

2. cube

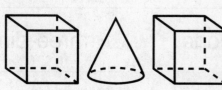

Circle the objects that match the description.

3. 6 faces, 8 vertices

4. 0 faces, 0 vertices

Write how many.

5.

___ faces

___ vertices

6.

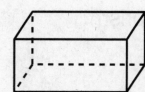

___ faces

___ vertices

7.

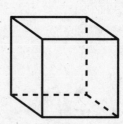

___ faces

___ vertices

8.

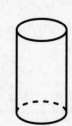

___ faces

___ vertices

Name _____

Vocabulary Test

Choose a word from the box to complete each sentence.

| cone | three-dimensional shape | cube |

1. A solid shape that is not flat is a

_____.

2. A three-dimensional shape with 6 square faces is a _____.

3. A three-dimensional shape that narrows to a point from a circular face is a _____.

Match the three-dimensional shape to its name.

4. rectanglar prism

5. cylinder

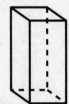

6. cube

Chapter Test, Form 1A

Circle the correct answer.

1. Which three-dimensional shape has 2 faces?

A.

B.

C.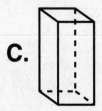

2. Which shape is a cone?

F.

G.

H.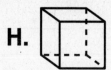

3. How many faces and vertices?

A. 6 faces
8 vertices

B. 2 faces
0 vertices

C. 1 face
1 vertex

4. How many faces and vertices?

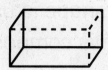

F. 1 face
1 vertex

G. 2 faces
0 vertices

H. 6 faces
8 vertices

GO on

Chapter Test, Form 1A (continued)

Circle the letter for the correct answer.

5. What is the shape of the faces of this object?

A. ◯

B. ▢

C. △

6. What object has the faces shown?

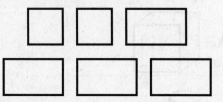

F.

G. 🎉

H. SOUP

7. Which shape is used to make this composite shape?

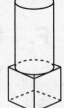

A. (cone)

B. (rectangular prism)

C. (cube)

8. Which three-dimensional shape is not used to make the composite shape shown?

F.

G. (rectangular prism)

H.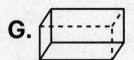

STOP

Name _____

Chapter Test, Form 1B

Circle the correct answer.

1. Which three-dimensional shape has 6 faces?

A.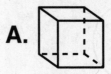

B.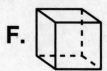

C.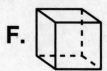

2. Which shape is a cylinder?

F.

G.

H.

3. How many faces and vertices?

A. 1 face
   1 vertex

B. 2 faces
   0 vertices

C. 6 faces
   8 vertices

4. How many faces and vertices?

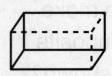

F. 6 faces
   8 vertices

G. 2 faces
   0 vertices

H. 1 face
   1 vertex

GO on

Chapter Test, Form 1B *(continued)*

Circle the correct answer.

5. What is the shape of the faces of this object?

A.

B.

C.

6. What object has the face shown?

F.

G.

H.

7. Which shape is used to make this composite shape?

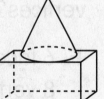

A.

B.

C.

8. Which three-dimensional shape is not used to make the composite shape shown?

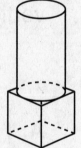

F.

G.

H.

Chapter Test, Form 2A

Circle the correct answer.

1. What is the name of this shape?

    A. cube

    B. cylinder

    C. rectangular prism

2. What is the name of this shape?

    F. cube

    G. cylinder

    H. cone

---

3. Which shape has 1 face and 1 vertex?

    A.

    B.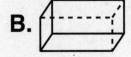

    C.

4. Which object has the faces shown?

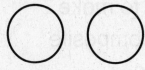

    F.

    G.

    H.

GO on

Chapter Test, Form 2A *(continued)*

Write the correct answer.

5. Circle the name of this three-dimensional shape.

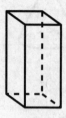

cube

rectangular prism

6. Write the number of faces and vertices.

_____ faces

_____ vertices

7. Circle the names of the shapes used to make this composite shape.

cone

cylinder

cube

8. Circle the shape of the faces of this object.

Chapter Test, Form 2B

Circle the correct answer.

1. What is the name of this shape?

A. rectangular prism

B. cylinder

C. cube

2. What is the name of this shape?

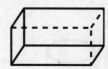

F. cone

G. cube

H. rectangluar prism

3. Which shape has 2 faces and 0 vertices?

A.

B.

C.

4. Which object has the faces shown?

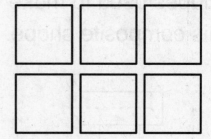

F.

G.

H.

GO on

Chapter Test, Form 2B *(continued)*

Write the correct answer.

5. Circle the name of this three-dimensional shape.

cylinder

cube

6. Write the number of faces and vertices.

_____ face

_____ vertex

7. Circle the names of the shapes used to make this composite shape.

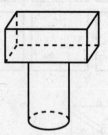

cube

rectangular prism

cylinder

8. Circle the shape of the face of this object.

Chapter Test, Form 3A

Identify each shape. Circle the name.
Write the number of faces and vertices.

1.    cylinder   cone

   _____ faces _____ vertices

2. 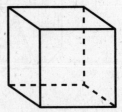   cube   rectangular prism

   _____ faces _____ vertices

Circle the shape of the faces that make each object.

3.  |

4.  |

Chapter Test, Form 3A *(continued)*

Circle the object that can be made by the faces.

5.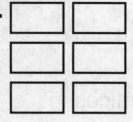

6.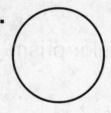

Circle the shapes used to make the composite shape.

7.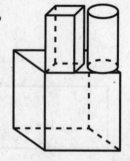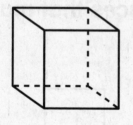

Circle the shape not used to make the composite shape.

8.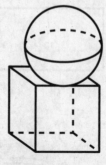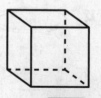

Name _____

Chapter Test, Form 3B

Identify each shape. Circle the name.
Write the number of faces and vertices.

1.    cylinder   cone

   _____ faces _____ vertices

2. 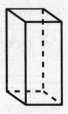   cube   rectangular prism

   _____ faces _____ vertices

Circle the shape of the faces that make each object.

3.

4.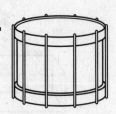

GO on

Chapter Test, Form 3B   *(continued)*

Circle the object that can be made by the faces.

5.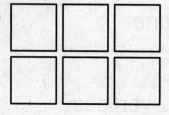

6.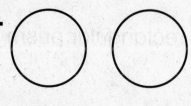

Circle the shapes used to make the composite shape.

7.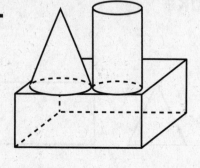

Circle the shape not used to make the composite shape.

8.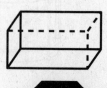

Name _____

Standardized Test Practice

Listen as your teacher reads each problem.
Choose the correct answer.

Example A

Which three-dimensional shape is a cube?

 ○

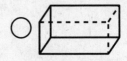 ○

 ○

○

Example B

Which three-dimensional shape is a cone?

○

○

○

○

---

1. How many faces and vertices does a rectangular prism have?

○ 1 face
    1 vertex

○ 2 faces
    0 vertices

○ 3 faces
    1 vertex

○ 6 faces
    8 vertices

2. How many faces and vertices does a cone have?

○ 1 face
    1 vertex

○ 2 faces
    0 vertices

○ 3 faces
    1 vertex

○ 6 faces
    8 vertices

GO on

Name _____

3. Which object can be made by the faces shown?

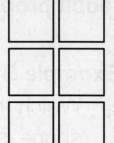

○

○

○

○

4. Which shape is used to make the composite shape?

○

○

○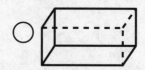

○

5. What is the shape of the faces that make up this object?

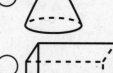

○

○

○ △

○ ▭

6. Which shape is not used to make the composite shape?

○ △

○ ▭

○

○ ▯

Name _____

 # Oral Assessment

Preparation: Geometric solids (cone, cylinder, cube, rectangular prism) are needed for this assessment.

Directions: This test targets those students who have developing verbal skills—both oral and written. Ask the questions below and have students record their answers, or record the answers they supply.

1. Set the geometric solids in front of the student. Say: *Point to the cone.* Ask: *How many faces and vertices does a cone have?*

2. Point to the cylinder. Ask: *What is the name of this three-dimensional shape?* Ask: *How many faces and vertices does this shape have?*

3. Say: *Point to the cube.* Ask: *How many faces and vertices does a cube have?* Say: *Draw the shape that makes up the faces of a cube.*

4. Point to the rectangular prism. Ask: *What is the name of this three-dimensional shape? How many faces and vertices does this shape have? What shapes make up the faces of this three-dimensional shape?*

5. Ask the student to put the geometric solids together to make a new composite shape. Ask: *What three-dimensional shapes did you use to make the composite shape?*

Notes

_____

_____

_____

_____

_____

_____

_____

Oral Assessment Response Sheet

1. _____

   _____

   _____

2. _____

   _____

   _____

3. _____

   _____

   _____

4. _____

   _____

   _____

5. _____

   _____

   _____

   _____

Listening Assessment

Directions: Ask students to perform the following tasks.

Preparation: Wooden geometric solids (cone, cylinder, cube, rectangluar prism) are needed for this assessment.

1. Write the number of faces and vertices of a cone.

2. Write the number of faces and vertices of a cylinder.

3. Write the number of faces and vertices of a cube.

4. Write the number of faces and vertices of a rectangular prism.

5. Draw the faces that make up a cube. Write the name of the shape.

6. Draw the faces that make up a cylinder. Write the name of the shape.

7. How are a cube and rectangular prism the same? How are they different? Write your answer.

Notes

_____

_____

_____

_____

_____

_____

_____

_____

Listening Assessment Response Sheet

1. _____

2. _____

3. _____

4. _____

5. _____

_____

6. _____

_____

7. _____

_____

_____

_____

Name _____

Benchmark Test I *(Chapters 1–2)*

Listen as your teacher reads each problem. Choose the correct answer.

Example A

How many are left?

○ 4   ○ 6
○ 7   ○ 8

Example B

How many umbrellas are there in all?

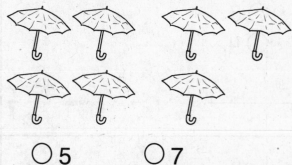

○ 5   ○ 7
○ 6   ○ 8

I. Which addition number sentence goes with this picture?

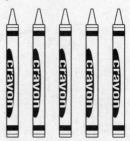 

○ 5 + 3 = 8
○ 6 + 4 = 10
○ 5 + 4 = 9
○ 6 + 5 = 11

2. Which subtraction sentence goes with this picture?

○ 8 − 2 = 7
○ 9 − 3 = 6
○ 9 − 4 = 5
○ 10 − 5 = 5

GO on

Name _____

Benchmark Test I   (Chapters 1–2)

**Listen as your teacher reads each problem.
Choose the correct answer.**

3. 4 + 1 = _____
- ○ 7
- ○ 6
- ○ 5
- ○ 4

4. 2 + 3 = _____
- ○ 4
- ○ 5
- ○ 6
- ○ 7

5. Miles found 3 rocks. He gave 1 to his brother. How many rocks does he have left?
- ○ 5
- ○ 4
- ○ 3
- ○ 2

6. Determine if the statement is true or false.

5 + 3 = 8
- ○ true
- ○ false

GO on

Benchmark Test I (Chapters 1–2)

Listen as your teacher reads each problem. Choose the correct answer.

7. Julia had 7 shirts. She gave 3 away. How many shirts does she have left?

- ○ 5
- ○ 4
- ○ 3
- ○ 2

8.
$$7$$
$$-\ 0$$

[ ]

- ○ 7
- ○ 6
- ○ 5
- ○ 4

9.
$$5$$
$$-\ 4$$

[ ]

- ○ 3
- ○ 2
- ○ I
- ○ 0

10. How many hearts are there in all?

- ○ 3
- ○ 6
- ○ 5
- ○ 7

STOP

Benchmark Test 2 *(Chapters 3–4)*

Listen as your teacher reads each problem. Choose the correct answer.

Example A

Use the number line to subtract. What is the difference?

0 1 2 3 4 5 6 7 8 9 10 11 12

11 – 2 = _____

○ 7   ○ 8
○ 9   ○ 10

Example B

Start with the greater number. Count on to add.

4 + 2 = _____

○ 4   ○ 5
○ 6   ○ 7

---

1. Rose had 5 pennies. She got 2 more. How many pennies does Rose have now?

○ 4   ○ 5
○ 6   ○ 7

2. Which subtraction number sentence goes with the story?

Kris sees 7 fish. 6 fish swim away. How many fish are left?

○ 7 – 3 = 4
○ 7 – 6 = 1
○ 7 – 5 = 2
○ 6 + 1 = 7

GO on

Benchmark Test 2 *(Chapters 3–4)*

Listen as your teacher reads each problem.
Choose the correct answer.

3. Add the doubles. Add the other number to find the sum.

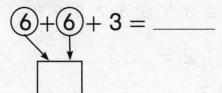

⑥+⑥+ 3 = _____

○ 15   ○ 13
○ 11   ○ 9

4. The puppy slept for 2 hours in the morning. He slept 2 hours after a walk and 1 hour before dinner. How many hours did the puppy sleep altogether?

○ 2   ○ 5
○ 4   ○ 6

5. What is the related subtraction fact?

5 + 2 = 7

○ 9 − 7 = 2
○ 9 − 5 = 4
○ 5 − 2 = 3
○ 7 − 5 = 2

6. Add the doubles fact. Then subtract. Which number shows the difference?

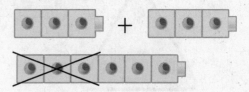

3 + 3 = 6

6 − 3 = _____

○ 4   ○ 3
○ 2   ○ 1

GO on

Benchmark Test 2   (Chapters 3–4)

Listen as your teacher reads each problem.
Choose the correct answer.

7. Which number sentence shows a missing addend?

○ $3 + 7 = \square$

○ $\square + 7 = 10$

8. Use the number line to add. Write the sum.

0 1 2 3 4 5 6 7 8 9 10 11 12

$7 + 2 =$ _____

○ 7
○ 8
○ 9
○ 10

9. Which subtraction number sentence is part of this fact family?

$4 + 5 = 9$
$5 + 4 = 9$
$9 - 5 = 4$

○ $9 - 3 = 6$
○ $9 + 5 = 14$
○ $9 - 4 = 5$
○ $9 - 2 = 7$

10.

1 2 3 4 5 6 7 8 9 10

Use the number line to subtract.

$8 - 3 =$ _____

○ 7
○ 6
○ 5
○ 4

STOP

Benchmark Test 3 *(Chapters 5–7)*

Listen as your teacher reads each problem.
Choose the correct answer.

Example A

5 tens + 1 ten = _____ tens

$$50 + 10 = \underline{}$$

○ 5 tens; 50

○ 6 tens; 60

○ 7 tens; 70

○ 8 tens; 80

Example B

What is the number?

tens	ones

forty-three

○ 43   ○ 34

○ 25   ○ 24

---

1. Ted is counting pennies. He has 7 groups of ten and 4 more. How many pennies does he have?

○ 11

○ 47

○ 70

○ 74

2. What is the missing number?

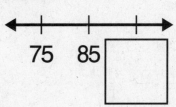

75   85

○ 86

○ 90

○ 95

○ 97

GO on

Benchmark Test 3   (Chapters 5–7)

Listen as your teacher reads each problem.
Choose the correct answer.

3. Count by tens. What is the number?

3 tens = _____
       thirty

○ 20   ○ 30

○ 40   ○ 50

4. How many  are there?

Animals at the Zoo		
Animal	Tally	Total
🐆	IIII	
🦭	HHH II	
🐘	HHH	

○ 5   ○ 6

○ 7   ○ 8

5. Compare.

56 ◯ 49

○ <

○ >

○ =

6. What is the answer?

17 + 5 = _____

tens	ones

○ 12   ○ 19

○ 22   ○ 32

GO on

Benchmark Test 3 (Chapters 5–7)

Listen as your teacher reads each problem.
Choose the correct answer.

7. How many more voted for 🍎 than 🍐?

Favorite Fruit

	0	1	2	3	4	5
🍎 Apple						
🍐 Pear						
🍌 Banana						

0 1 2 3 4 5

○ 1   ○ 2
○ 3   ○ 4

8. What is the number?

hundreds	tens	ones

hundreds	tens	ones
___	___	___

_____

one hundred twenty-four

○ 104   ○ 114
○ 124   ○ 142

9. Subtract. What is the related addition fact?

$80 - 50 = $ _____

○ $50 + 20 = 70$

○ $20 + 60 = 80$

○ $50 + 30 = 80$

○ $50 + 40 = 90$

10. Count. How many tens and ones?

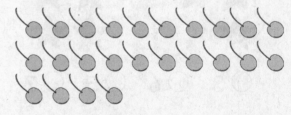

○ one ten and four ones

○ one ten and fourteen ones

○ two tens and four ones

○ twenty-four ones

STOP

Benchmark Test 4   (Chapters 1–10)

Listen as your teacher reads each question.
Choose the correct answer.

Example A

How many birds in all?

○ 3   ○ 5   ○ 6   ○ 8

Example B

Count back to subtract.
Start with 5.

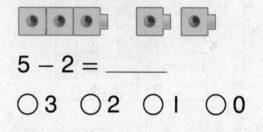

$5 - 2 =$ _____

○ 3   ○ 2   ○ 1   ○ 0

---

1. How many stars are there in all?

○ 3   ○ 6   ○ 5   ○ 7

2. Count on to add.

$4 + 3 =$ _____

○ 4
○ 5
○ 6
○ 7

---

3. Count by tens. What is the number?

2 tens = _____
              twenty

○ 20   ○ 40
○ 60   ○ 80

GO on

Benchmark Test 4 *(Chapters 1–10)*

4. Subtract.

6 tens − 2 tens = _____ tens

60 − 20 = _____

- ○ 3 tens; 30
- ○ 4 tens, 40
- ○ 5 tens, 50
- ○ 6 tens, 60

5. How many are there?

Animals at the Zoo		
Animal	Tally	Total
	IIII	
	HHT II	
	HHT	

○ 5 ○ 6 ○ 7 ○ 8

6. Which ribbon is the longest?

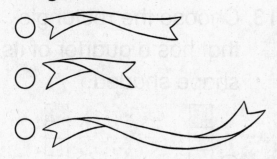

○

○

○

7. How many sides and vertices does a circle have?

- ○ 0 sides and 0 vertices
- ○ 3 sides and 3 vertices
- ○ 4 sides and 4 vertices
- ○ 4 sides and 2 vertices

8. Which object can be made by the faces below?

○   ○

○   ○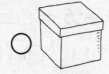

9. What time is it?

- ○ 10 o'clock
- ○ half past 10
- ○ 11 o'clock
- ○ half past 11

GO on

Benchmark Test 4   (Chapters 1–10)

10. Which pattern block was used to make the shape.

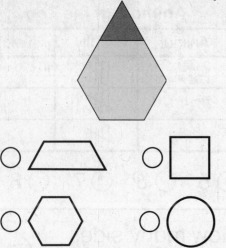

○ ⬡ (trapezoid)   ○ ☐ (square)

○ ⬡ (hexagon)   ○ ◯ (circle)

11. What is the shape of the faces that make up the object?

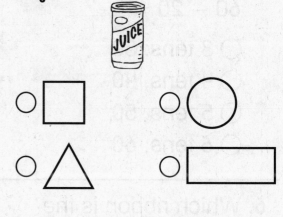

○ ☐   ○ ◯

○ △   ○ ▭

12. Which shape is not used to make the composite shape?

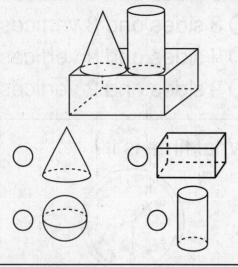

○ (cone)   ○ (rectangular prism)

○ (sphere)   ○ (cylinder)

13. Choose the rectangle that has a quarter of its shape shaded.

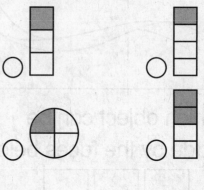

14. Subtract.

$5 - 4 =$ _____

○ 3   ○ 2   ○ 1   ○ 0

15. Add.

$5 + 6 =$ _____

○ 11   ○ 10   ○ 9   ○ 8

GO on

Benchmark Test 4   (Chapters 1–10)

16. What is the related subtraction fact?

$7 + 7 = 14$

○ $14 - 7 = 7$
○ $15 - 9 = 6$
○ $16 - 8 = 8$
○ $17 - 9 = 6$

17. Count from 29 to 35. What number comes next?

1	2	3	4	5	6	7	8	9	10
11	12	13	14	15	16	17	18	19	20
21	22	23	24	25	26	27	28	29	30
31	32	33	34	35	36	37	38	39	40

○ 36   ○ 29
○ 38   ○ 19

18. Subtract.

```
  9 tens          90
- 2 tens        - 20
_____ tens    _____
```

○ 7 tens, 70
○ 5 tens, 50
○ 2 tens, 20
○ 1 tens, 10

19. Look at the tally chart. How many more people voted for the ○ than the ★?

Favorite Shape		
Shape	Tally	Total
○ Circle	⊞⊞ ‖	
★ Star	⊞⊞	
△ Triangle	⊞⊞	

○ 2   ○ 3   ○ 4   ○ 5

20. Which fish is the shortest?

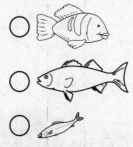

○

○

○

GO on

Benchmark Test 4 (Chapters 1–10)

21. How many sides and vertices does a rectangle have?

○ 0 sides and 0 vertices
○ 3 sides and 3 vertices
○ 4 sides and 4 vertices
○ 4 sides and 0 vertices

22. Which shape is used to make the composite shape?

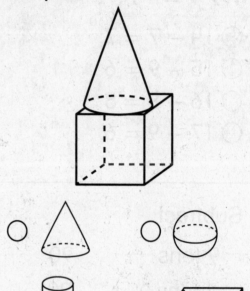

○ △   ○ ⊘

○ ▯   ○ ▭

23. Count by fives. How much in all?

○ 30¢
○ 25¢
○ 20¢
○ 15¢

24. Add the doubles. Add the other number to find the sum.

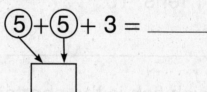

$5 + 5 + 3 =$ _____

○ 15
○ 13
○ 11
○ 9

GO on

Benchmark Test 4 (Chapters 1–10)

25. What time is it?

○ half past 9
○ 9 o'clock
○ half past 8

26. What time is it?

○ 6 o'clock
○ 7 o'clock
○ half past 7

27. Which shape is a square?

○

○

○

○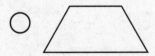

28. Which three-dimensional shape is the cube?

○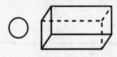

○

○

○

29. Subtract. What is the related addition fact?

$$80 - 50 = \underline{\qquad}$$

○ $50 + 20 = 70$
○ $20 + 60 = 80$
○ $50 + 30 = 80$
○ $50 + 40 = 90$

30. About how many cubes long is the pencil?

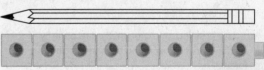

○ about 7 cubes
○ about 8 cubes
○ about 9 cubes

Name _____

Am I Ready?

Practice

Write how many.

1.   __2__

2.   __8__

Draw circles to show each number.

3. 3 ◯ ◯ ◯

4. 1 ◯

5. 9 ◯ ◯ ◯ ◯ ◯ ◯ ◯ ◯ ◯

Use 🎲 to show how many. Write how many there are in all.

6. __7__ in all

Name _____

Am I Ready?

Review

> The number 5 shows that there are 5 trucks.
>
> __5__

Write how many.

1.   __7__

2.   __2__

3.   __8__

4.   __4__

5.   __1__

Name _____

Am I Ready?

Apply

Use 🎲 to show how many. Write how many in all.

1. 4 brown dogs are playing. 2 white dogs come to play, too. How many dogs are playing?
   __6__

2. 7 frogs are sitting on a lily pad. 1 more frog jumps on the lily pad. How many frogs are there altogether?
   __8__

3. 6 bees sit on a flower. 3 more bees come to the flower. How many bees are there in all?
   __9__

4. 1 bird is sitting on a branch. 3 more birds fly to the branch. How many birds are on the branch?
   __4__

5. 5 turtles are on a rock. 1 more turtle joins them. How many turtles are there altogether?
   __6__

Name _____

Diagnostic Test

Am I Ready for the Chapter?

Write how many.

1.   __4__

2.   __7__

Draw stars to show each number.

3. 6   ★★★★★★

4. 8   ★★★★★★★★

5. 11   ★★★★★★★★★★★

Solve.

6. Write how many balloons are there in all.

__9__ in all

Name _____

Pretest

Write addition number sentences.

1.

4 plus 2 equals __6__.

__4__ ⊕ __2__ ⊜ __6__

2.

3 plus 4 equals __7__.

__3__ ⊕ __4__ ⊜ __7__

3.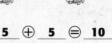

__5__ ⊕ __5__ ⊜ __10__

4.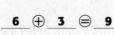

__6__ ⊕ __3__ ⊜ __9__

Write the numbers. Add.

5.

$\begin{array}{r} 3 \\ + 2 \\ \hline 5 \end{array}$

6.

$\begin{array}{r} 4 \\ + 3 \\ \hline 7 \end{array}$

Name _____

Check My Progress *(Lessons 1 through 4)*

Add. Write the number.

Part	Part
2	4
Whole	
6	

1. parts: 2 and 3; whole: __5__

2. parts: 3 and 4; whole: __7__

3. What is the sum?

2 + 4 = __6__

4. Write the addition number sentence.

__3__ ⊕ __4__ ⊜ __7__

5. There are 3 white horses and 5 brown horses. How many horses are there in all?

__3__ ⊕ __5__ ⊜ __8__ horses

Name _____

Check My Progress *(Lessons 5 through 9)*

Add. Write the numbers.

1.

[3] + [4] = [7]

2.

$\begin{array}{r} 6 \\ 2 \\ \hline 8 \end{array}$

3. 3 + 3 = __6__

4. 2 + 5 = __7__

5. $\begin{array}{r} 4 \\ + 4 \\ \hline 8 \end{array}$

6. $\begin{array}{r} 1 \\ + 6 \\ \hline 7 \end{array}$

Write an addition number sentence to solve.

7. Jamie has 3 red beads and 5 blue beads. How many beads are there in all?

__3 + 5 = 8__   __8__ beads

8. Walter has 2 toy cars and 3 toy trucks. How many toys does he have in all?

__2 + 3 = 5__   __5__ toy cars

Name _____

Vocabulary Test

Write the correct word(s) in the blank.
Use the words from the box.

> add   addition number sentence
> equals (=)   plus (+)   sum

1. When you join parts together to find the sum, you __add__.

2. The sign used to show having the same value is called __equals (=)__.

3. The symbol used to show addition is called the __plus (+)__ sign.

4. An expression using numbers and the + and = sign is called an __addition number sentence__.

5. The answer to an addition sentence is called the __sum__.

Answers

Answers (Forms 1A and 1B)

Chapter Test, Form 1A

Circle the correct answer.

1. How many apples in all?

(A.) 5
B. 6
C. 3

2. Which addition number sentence goes with the picture?

F. 5 + 2 = 3
G. 5 + 3 = 8
(H.) 5 + 2 = 7

3. 2 + 3 = ☐

A. 4
(B.) 5
C. 8

4. Determine if the statement is true or false.

1 + 6 = 6

F. true
(G.) false

Grade 1 • **Chapter 1** Addition Concepts   15

Chapter Test, Form 1A   (continued)

5. 7
       + 2

(A.) 9
B. 5
C. 4

6. 8
       + 2

F. 2
G. 8
(H.) 10

7. Add the two parts.

Part	Part
5	1
Whole	
___	

A. 2
B. 5
(C.) 6

8. What is the sum?

3 + 0 = ____

F. 0
(G.) 3
H. 5

16   Grade 1 • **Chapter 1** Addition Concepts

Chapter Test, Form 1B

Circle the correct answer.

1. How many bananas in all?

A. 4
(B.) 5
C. 7

2. Which addition number sentence goes with this picture?

(F.) 4 + 5 = 9
G. 5 + 4 = 10
H. 6 + 4 = 11

3. 3 + 2 = ☐

A. 6
B. 3
(C.) 5

4. 7 + 1 = ☐

F. 9
(G.) 8
H. 10

Grade 1 • **Chapter 1** Addition Concepts   17

Chapter Test, Form 1B   (continued)

5. 4 + 3 = ☐

A. 11
B. 9
(C.) 7

6. Determine if the statement is true or false.

6 + 4 = 10

(F.) true
G. false

7. Add the two parts.

Part	Part
3	2
Whole	
___	

A. 7
B. 4
(C.) 5

8. What is the sum?

4 + 0 = ____

(F.) 4
G. 6
H. 3

18   Grade 1 • **Chapter 1** Addition Concepts

A3   **Grade 1 • Chapter 1** Addition Concepts

Answers (Forms 2A and 2B)

Name _____

Chapter Test, Form 2A

Circle the correct answer.

1. How many peppers in all?

A. 3
B. 5
C. 7 (circled)
D. 8

2. Which addition number sentence matches the picture?

F. 2 + 7 = 9
G. 2 + 6 = 8 (circled)
H. 0 + 6 = 6
I. 4 + 8 = 12

3. 3 + 1 = ☐

A. 4 (circled)
B. 5
C. 6
D. 7

4. 3 + 5 = ☐

F. 5
G. 6
H. 7
I. 8 (circled)

5. 5 + 4 = ☐

A. 8
B. 9 (circled)
C. 10
D. 11

6. Determine if the statement is true or false.

7 + 3 = 9

F. true
G. false (circled)

GO on

Grade 1 • **Chapter 1** Addition Concepts   19

Name _____

Chapter Test, Form 2A (continued)

Read each question carefully. Write your answer on the line provided.

7. Find the sum of the parts. Write the whole.

Part	Part
6	2
Whole	

8

8. What is the sum?

5 + 0 = __5__

9. Edward has 2 pairs of black shoes and 1 pair of brown shoes. How many pairs of shoes does he have in all? Write an addition number sentence.

__2__ + __1__ = __3__

10. Write the addition number sentence that matches the picture.

__4__ + __6__ = __10__

 STOP

20   Grade 1 • **Chapter 1** Addition Concepts

Name _____

Chapter Test, Form 2B

Circle the correct answer.

1. How many flowers in all?

A. 5
B. 8 (circled)
C. 7
D. 10

2. Which addition number sentence matches the picture?

F. 4 + 5 = 9 (circled)
G. 3 + 6 = 9
H. 4 + 0 = 4
I. 6 + 7 = 13

3. 4 + 2 = ☐

A. 4
B. 5
C. 6 (circled)
D. 7

4. 5 + 4 = ☐

F. 8
G. 9 (circled)
H. 10
I. 11

5. 2
  + 5

A. 7 (circled)
B. 8
C. 10
D. 11

6. Determine if the statement is true or false.

3 + 5 = 7

F. true
G. false (circled)

GO on

Grade 1 • **Chapter 1** Addition Concepts   21

Name _____

Chapter Test, Form 2B (continued)

Read each question carefully. Write your answer on the line provided.

7. Find the sum of the two parts. Write the whole.

Part	Part
5	2
Whole	

7

8. What is the sum?

7 + 0 = __7__

9. Lin has 3 red shirts and 4 green shirts. How many shirts does Lin have? Write an addition number sentence.

__3__ + __4__ = __7__

10. Write the addition number sentence that matches the picture.

__2__ + __8__ = __10__

 STOP

22   Grade 1 • **Chapter 1** Addition Concepts

Answers (Forms 3A and 3B)

Name _____

Chapter Test, Form 3A

Write the correct answer.

1. How many ladybugs in all?

__9__

2. Write the addition number sentence that matches the picture.

__4__ + __3__ = __7__

3. $4 + 1 =$ ⬚5

4. $0 + 6 =$ ⬚6

5. $6 + 2 =$ ⬚8

6. Determine if the statement is true or false.

$2 + 6 = 8$

(true)　　　false

 GO on

Grade 1 • **Chapter 1** Addition Concepts　　23

Name _____

Chapter Test, Form 3A *(continued)*

7. Find the sum of the two parts. Write the whole.

Part	Part
5	4
Whole	
9	

8. 3 penguins are on the ice. 2 more penguins run to join them. How many penguins altogether? Write the correct addition number sentence.

__3__ + __2__ = __5__

9. Write the addition number sentence that matches the counters.

__2__ + __8__ = __10__

10. What is the sum?

$6 + 0 =$ __6__

11. Akio sees 7 ants. He sees 3 more ants coming. How many ants are there now? Write the addition number sentence across and down to solve.

⬚7 + ⬚3 = ⬚10

```
   7
+  3
  10
```

STOP

24　　Grade 1 • **Chapter 1** Addition Concepts

Name _____

Chapter Test, Form 3B

Write the correct answer.

1. How many snails in all?

__10__

2. Write the addition number sentence that goes with the picture.

__2__ + __5__ = __7__

3. $3 + 3 =$ ⬚6

4. $9 + 0 =$ ⬚9

5. $2 + 5 =$ ⬚7

6. Determine if the statement is true or false.

$8 + 2 = 11$

true　　　(false)

 GO on

Grade 1 • **Chapter 1** Addition Concepts　　25

Name _____

Chapter Test, Form 3B *(continued)*

7. Add the two parts. Write the whole.

Part	Part
●●●	○○○○○
Whole	
8	

8. 6 cows are eating. 3 more cows join them. How many cows are eating now? Write the addition number sentence.

__6__ + __3__ = __9__

9. Write the addition number sentence that goes with the counters.

__4__ + __6__ = __10__

10. What is the sum?

$5 + 0 =$ __5__

11. Jill had 3 fish. She gets 4 more. How many fish does Jill have now? Write the addition number sentence across and down to solve.

⬚3 + ⬚4 = ⬚7

```
   3
+  4
   7
```

STOP

26　　Grade 1 • **Chapter 1** Addition Concepts

A5

Grade 1 • Chapter 1 Addition Concepts

Name _____

Standardized Test Practice

Listen as your teacher reads each problem.
Choose the correct answer.

Example A

How many turtles are there in all?

○ 4   ○ 8
● 5   ○ 9

Example B

How many umbrellas are there in all?

○ 5   ● 7
○ 6   ○ 8

1. How many hearts are there in all?

○ 3   ○ 6
○ 5   ● 7

2. Which addition number sentence goes with this picture?

● 5 + 3 = 8
○ 6 + 4 = 10
○ 5 + 4 = 9
○ 6 + 5 = 11

GO on

Name _____

Standardized Test Practice *(continued)*

Listen as your teacher reads each problem.
Choose the correct answer.

3. 3 + 3 = _____
● 6
○ 3
○ 5
○ 7

4. 8 + 1 = _____
○ 1
○ 8
● 9
○ 10

5. 3 + 2 = _____
○ 4
● 5
○ 6
○ 7

6. 4 + 1 = _____
○ 7
○ 6
● 5
○ 4

STOP

Name _____

Oral Assessment Response Sheet

1. ___**7 counters**___   2. ___**5**___

3. ___**2 + 4 = 6**___   4. ___**3 + 6 = 9**___

5. ___**8**___   6. ___**6**___

7. ___**7**___   8. ___**10**___

9. ___**See students' work.**___

Name _____

Listening Assessment Response Sheet

1. ___**8 counters**___

2. ___**See students' drawings.**___
   __3__ ⊕ __4__ ⊜ __7__ stars

3. ___**6**___

4. __4__ ⊕ __1__ ⊜ __5__

5.
●	●	●	●	●
○	○	○	○	○

   __5__ ⊕ __5__ ⊜ __10__

6. ___**See students' drawings.**___
   __3__ ⊕ __2__ ⊜ __5__

A6

Answers

Name _____

Am I Ready?

Practice

Write how many.

1. 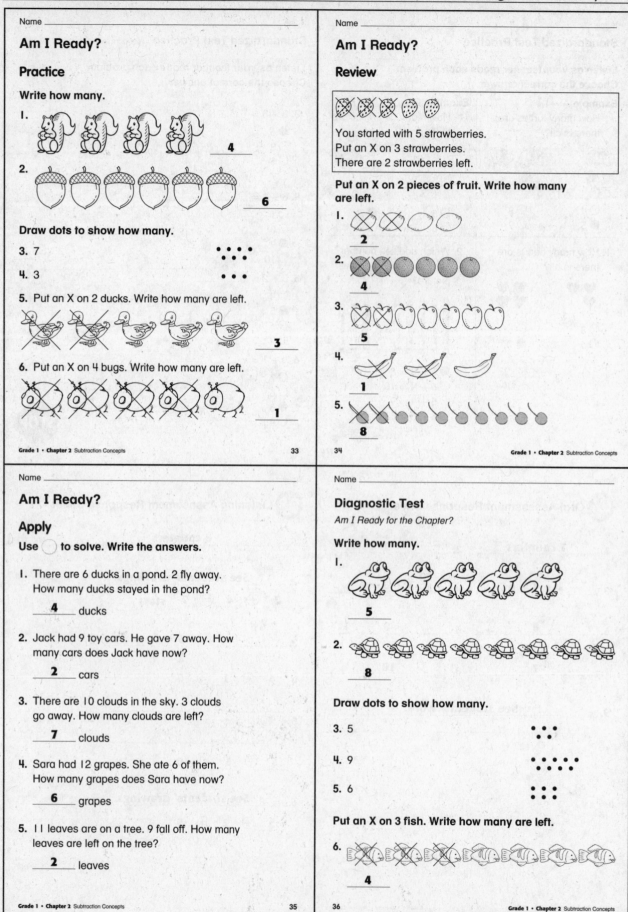   **4**

2. **6**

Draw dots to show how many.

3. 7

4. 3

5. Put an X on 2 ducks. Write how many are left.

   3

6. Put an X on 4 bugs. Write how many are left.

   1

Name _____

Am I Ready?

Review

You started with 5 strawberries.
Put an X on 3 strawberries.
There are 2 strawberries left.

Put an X on 2 pieces of fruit. Write how many are left.

1. **2**

2. **4**

3. **5**

4. **1**

5. **8**

Name _____

Am I Ready?

Apply

Use ◯ to solve. Write the answers.

1. There are 6 ducks in a pond. 2 fly away. How many ducks stayed in the pond?

   _____**4**_____ ducks

2. Jack had 9 toy cars. He gave 7 away. How many cars does Jack have now?

   _____**2**_____ cars

3. There are 10 clouds in the sky. 3 clouds go away. How many clouds are left?

   _____**7**_____ clouds

4. Sara had 12 grapes. She ate 6 of them. How many grapes does Sara have now?

   _____**6**_____ grapes

5. 11 leaves are on a tree. 9 fall off. How many leaves are left on the tree?

   _____**2**_____ leaves

Name _____

Diagnostic Test

Am I Ready for the Chapter?

Write how many.

1. **5**

2. **8**

Draw dots to show how many.

3. 5

4. 9

5. 6

Put an X on 3 fish. Write how many are left.

6. **4**

Name _____

Pretest

Write the subtraction number sentence.

1.

$\underline{6}$ ⊖ $\underline{2}$ ⊜ $\underline{4}$

2.

$\underline{8}$ ⊖ $\underline{3}$ ⊜ $\underline{5}$

Solve.

3. 5 apples grew on a tree. 2 fell off. How many apples are left? $\underline{3}$

4. 9 − 4 = $\underline{5}$　　5. 7 − 0 = $\underline{7}$

6. 10 − 4 = $\underline{6}$　　7. 3 − 3 = $\underline{0}$

Name _____

Check My Progress　(Lessons 1 through 5)

Write the subtraction number sentence.

1.

$\underline{6}$ ⊖ $\underline{2}$ ⊜ $\underline{4}$

2.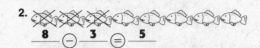

$\underline{8}$ ⊖ $\underline{3}$ ⊜ $\underline{5}$

3. There are 9 frogs on a log. 4 frogs jump off the log. How many frogs are left on the log?

$\underline{5}$ frogs

4. There are 7 birds sitting in the tree. 7 of the birds fly away. How many birds are left in the tree?

$\underline{0}$ birds

Subtract.

5. 　$\begin{array}{r} 9 \\ -4 \\ \hline \boxed{5} \end{array}$　6. 　$\begin{array}{r} 8 \\ -5 \\ \hline \boxed{3} \end{array}$

Name _____

Check My Progress　(Lessons 6 through 9)

Write the subtraction number sentence.

1.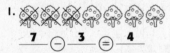

$\underline{7}$ ⊖ $\underline{3}$ ⊜ $\underline{4}$

Subtract.

2. 6 − 3 = $\underline{3}$　　3. 5 − 5 = $\underline{0}$

4. $\begin{array}{r} 8 \\ -4 \\ \hline \boxed{4} \end{array}$　　5. $\begin{array}{r} 7 \\ -2 \\ \hline \boxed{5} \end{array}$

Write the subtraction number sentence.

6. 6 birds are blue. 2 birds are red. How many less birds are red than blue?

$\underline{6}$ − $\underline{2}$ = $\underline{4}$ birds

7. 8 apples are green. 3 apples are red. How many more apples are green than red?

$\underline{8}$ − $\underline{3}$ = $\underline{5}$ apples

Name _____

Vocabulary Test

Circle the correct answer.

1. 9 − 7 = 2 is a _____.
   A. sum　　　　　Ⓒ. subtraction number sentence
   B. difference　　D. equals

2. When you take away, you _____.
   F. add　　　　　H. difference
   Ⓖ. subtract　　 I. plus

3. 7 − 4 = 3
   In this problem, the 3 is called the _____.
   Ⓐ. difference　　C. minus
   B. sum　　　　　D. subtraction number sentence

4. 2 + 4 = 6 and 6 − 4 = 2 are called _____ because they use the same numbers.
   F. sum　　　　　H. subtraction number sentence
   G. difference　　Ⓘ. related facts

5. The sign used to show subtraction is called the _____ sign.
   A. difference　　Ⓒ. minus (−)
   B. sum　　　　　D. plus (+)

Answers

Answers (Forms 1A and 1B)

Name _____

Chapter Test, Form 1A

Read each question. Circle the correct answer.

1. Ann has 6 buckets. 5 have sand in them. How many buckets are empty?

   (A.) 1   **B.** 6   **C.** 7

2. There are 4 tigers. There is 1 lion. How many fewer lions are there than tigers?

   F. 3 − 2 = 1 fewer lion

   (G.) 4 − 1 = 3 fewer lions

   H. 4 − 2 = 2 fewer lions

3. Look at the addition number sentence below. Which of the following shows a related subtraction fact?

   1 + 7 = 8

   (A.) 8 − 7 = 1   **B.** 7 − 1 = 6   **C.** 8 + 1 = 9

4. What is the difference?

Part	Part
4	
Whole	
6	

   F. 10
   G. 3
   (H.) 2

Grade 1 • **Chapter 2** Subtraction Concepts   41

Name _____

Chapter Test, Form 1A *(continued)*

Circle the the correct answer.

5. 10 − 0 =

   A. 1
   B. 9
   (C.) 10

6. 4 − 3 =

   (F.) 1
   G. 0
   H. 2

7. 8
   − 8
   ____

   (A.) 0
   B. 7
   C. 1

8. 9
   − 4
   ____

   F. 6
   G. 4
   (H.) 5

9. Which subtraction number sentence goes with the picture?

   A. 5 − 0 = 5
   (B.) 5 − 2 = 3
   C. 3 − 2 = 1

10. Which subtraction number sentence goes with the picture?

   (F.) 7 − 1 = 6
   G. 6 − 1 = 5
   H. 6 + 1 = 7

STOP

42   Grade 1 • **Chapter 2** Subtraction Concepts

Name _____

Chapter Test, Form 1B

Read each question. Circle the correct answer.

1. Leo buys 4 buttons. 1 button has stripes. How many buttons do not have stripes?

   A. 1   **B.** 2   **(C.)** 3

2. There are 6 snakes. There are 2 frogs. How many fewer frogs are there than snakes?

   F. 4 − 4 = 0 fewer frogs

   (G.) 6 − 2 = 4 fewer frogs

   H. 6 − 3 = 3 fewer frogs

3. Look at the addition number sentence below. Which of the following shows a related subtraction fact?

   4 + 3 = 7

   A. 7 − 1 = 6   **B.** 4 − 3 = 1   **(C.)** 7 − 3 = 4

4. What is the difference?

Part	Part
1	
Whole	
2	

   (F.) 1
   G. 2
   H. 3

Grade 1 • **Chapter 2** Subtraction Concepts   43

Name _____

Chapter Test, Form 1B *(continued)*

Circle the correct answer.

5. 9 − 1 =

   A. 9
   (B.) 8
   C. 0

6. 6 − 0 =

   F. 2
   G. 5
   (H.) 6

7. 9
   − 8
   ____

   A. 7
   B. 2
   (C.) 1

8. 5
   − 5
   ____

   F. 10
   G. 5
   (H.) 0

9. Which subtraction number sentence goes with the picture?

   A. 5 − 5 = 5
   (B.) 5 − 4 = 1
   C. 5 + 4 = 9

10. Which subtraction number sentence goes with the picture?

   F. 5 − 3 = 2
   G. 8 − 0 = 8
   (H.) 8 − 5 = 3

STOP

44   Grade 1 • **Chapter 2** Subtraction Concepts

A9

Grade 1 • Chapter 2 Subtraction Concepts

Name _____

Chapter Test, Form 2A

Circle the correct answer.

1. There are 5 birds. 1 flies away. How many birds are left?

A. 7
B. 6
C. 5
(D.) 4

2. There are 6 flowers. There are 4 bees. How many more flowers are there than bees?

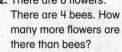

F. 4 − 3 = 1 more flower
G. 8 − 7 = 1 more flower
(H.) 6 − 4 = 2 more flowers
I. 10 − 6 = 4 more flowers

3. Look at the addition number sentence below. Which of the following show a related subtraction fact?

5 + 3 = 8
A. 8 − 1 = 7
B. 5 − 3 = 2
C. 8 − 4 = 4
(D.) 8 − 3 = 5

4. What is the difference?

Part	Part
1	
Whole	
8	

F. 1
G. 3
(H.) 7
I. 9

Grade 1 • **Chapter 2** Subtraction Concepts
45

46

Name _____

Chapter Test, Form 2A *(continued)*

Read each question. Write the answer.

5.
```
  7
− 5
───
  2
```

6.
```
  9
− 9
───
  0
```

7. Write the subtraction number sentence that goes with the picture.

6 ⊖ 2 ⊜ 4

8. Write the subtraction number sentence that goes with the picture.

10 ⊖ 8 ⊜ 2

 STOP

Grade 1 • **Chapter 2** Subtraction Concepts

Name _____

Chapter Test, Form 2B

Read each question. Circle the correct answer.

1. There are 6 cats. 1 runs away. How many are left?

A. 1
(B.) 5
C. 6
D. 7

2. There are 7 flowers. There are 2 bees. How many more flowers are there than bees?

F. 5 + 2 = 7 more flowers
G. 2 + 5 = 7 more flowers
H. 7 − 5 = 2 more flowers
(I.) 7 − 2 = 5 more flowers

3. Look at the addition number sentence below. Which of the following shows a related subtraction fact?

4 + 5 = 9
A. 9 + 4 = 13
(B.) 9 − 5 = 4
C. 5 − 4 = 1
D. 9 − 6 = 3

4. What is the difference?

Part	Part
2	
Whole	
5	

F. 0
G. 1
H. 2
(I.) 3

Grade 1 • **Chapter 2** Subtraction Concepts
47

48

Name _____

Chapter Test, Form 2B *(continued)*

Read each question. Write the answer.

5.
```
  8
− 4
───
  4
```

6.
```
  5
− 5
───
  0
```

7. Write the subtraction number sentence that goes with the picture.

7 ⊖ 3 ⊜ 4

8. Write the subtraction number sentence that goes with the picture.

6 ⊖ 2 ⊜ 4

STOP

Grade 1 • **Chapter 2** Subtraction Concepts

Grade 1 • Chapter 2 Subtraction Concepts

A10

Answers (Forms 3A and 3B)

Name _____

Chapter Test, Form 3A

Read each question. Write the correct answer.

1. There are 5 butterflies.
3 fly away.
How many butterflies
are left?

__**2**__ butterflies

2. There are 7 marbles.
There is one beach ball.
How many fewer beach
balls are there than
marbles?

__**6**__ fewer beach balls

3. Look at the addition
number sentence below.
Write a related subtraction
number sentence.

$1 + 7 = 8$

__**8**__ – __**7**__ = __**1**__
or
__**8**__ – __**1**__ = __**7**__

4. What is the difference?

Part	Part
4	
Whole	
6	

$6 - 4 =$ __**2**__

5. Write a subtraction number sentence to match the picture.

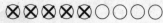

__**9**__ ⊖ __**5**__ ⊜ __**4**__

 GO on

Grade 1 • **Chapter 2** Subtraction Concepts   **49**

Name _____

Chapter Test, Form 3A *(continued)*

6. $5 - 4 =$ __**1**__   **7.** $7 - 3 =$ __**4**__

8.
$$\begin{array}{r} 9 \\ -\,6 \\ \hline 3 \end{array}$$

9. Write the subtraction
number sentence.

__**10**__ ⊖ __**8**__ ⊜ __**2**__

10. Georgia made 10 bracelets.
She gave 8 of them away.
How many bracelets does
she have left?

__**2**__ bracelets

$$\begin{array}{r} \boxed{10} \\ -\;\boxed{8} \\ \hline \boxed{2} \end{array}$$

11. $9 - 6 =$ __**3**__   **12.**
$$\begin{array}{r} 7 \\ -\,3 \\ \hline 4 \end{array}$$

STOP

50   Grade 1 • **Chapter 2** Subtraction Concepts

Name _____

Chapter Test, Form 3B

Read each question. Write the correct answer.

1. There are 4 birds.
1 flies away.
How many are there
now?

__**3**__ birds

2. There are 8 hot dogs.
There are 4 hamburgers.
How many fewer
hamburgers are there
than hot dogs?

__**4**__ fewer hamburgers

3. Look at the addition
number sentence below.
Write a related subtraction
number sentence.

$5 + 2 = 7$

__**7**__ – __**2**__ = __**5**__
or
__**7**__ – __**5**__ = __**2**__

4. What is the difference?

Part	Part
0	
Whole	
8	

$8 - 0 =$ __**8**__

5. Write the subtraction sentence to match the picture.

__**6**__ ⊖ __**4**__ ⊜ __**2**__

 GO on

Grade 1 • **Chapter 2** Subtraction Concepts   **51**

Name _____

Chapter Test, Form 3B *(continued)*

6. $9 - 1 =$ __**8**__   **7.**
$$\begin{array}{r} 8 \\ -\,4 \\ \hline 4 \end{array}$$

8.
$$\begin{array}{r} 9 \\ -\,5 \\ \hline 4 \end{array}$$

9. Write the subtraction
sentence.

__**10**__ ⊖ __**9**__ ⊜ __**1**__

10. John played catch with his dad. His dad
threw the ball 10 times. John caught it
8 times. How many times did John miss
a catch?

__**10**__ ⊖ __**8**__ ⊜ __**2**__

11.
$$\begin{array}{r} 6 \\ -\,3 \\ \hline 3 \end{array}$$

12. $10 - 4 =$ __**6**__

STOP

52   Grade 1 • **Chapter 2** Subtraction Concepts

Grade 1 • Chapter 2 Subtraction Concepts

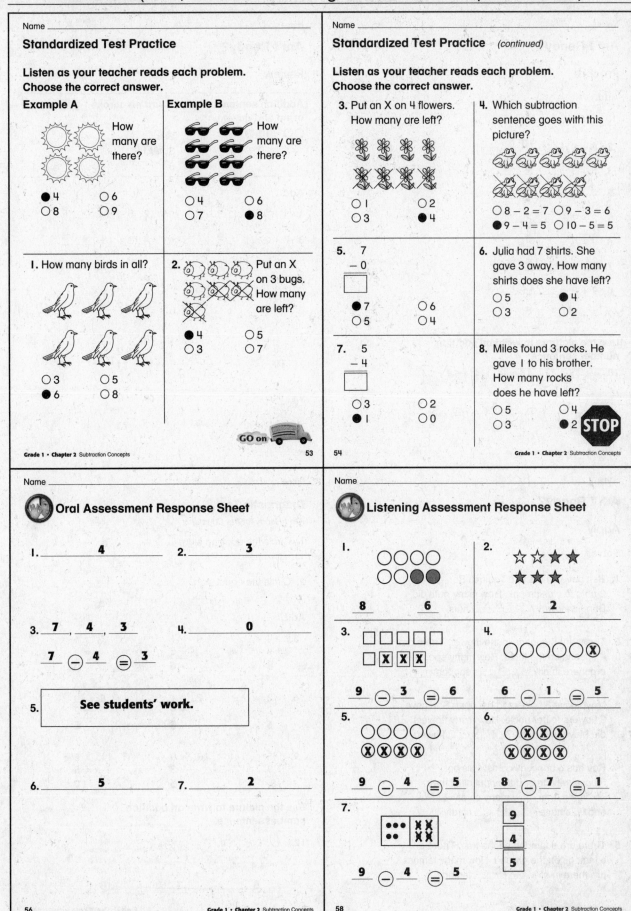

Name _____

Standardized Test Practice

Listen as your teacher reads each problem.
Choose the correct answer.

Example A

How many are there?

● 4   ○ 6
○ 8   ○ 9

Example B

How many are there?

○ 4   ○ 6
○ 7   ● 8

1. How many birds in all?

○ 3   ○ 5
● 6   ○ 8

2. Put an X on 3 bugs. How many are left?

● 4   ○ 5
○ 3   ○ 7

GO on

Grade 1 • Chapter 2 Subtraction Concepts   53

Name _____

Standardized Test Practice   *(continued)*

Listen as your teacher reads each problem.
Choose the correct answer.

3. Put an X on 4 flowers. How many are left?

○ 1   ○ 2
○ 3   ● 4

4. Which subtraction sentence goes with this picture?

○ 8 − 2 = 7   ○ 9 − 3 = 6
● 9 − 4 = 5   ○ 10 − 5 = 5

5. 7
   − 0
   ☐

● 7   ○ 6
○ 5   ○ 4

6. Julia had 7 shirts. She gave 3 away. How many shirts does she have left?

○ 5   ● 4
○ 3   ○ 2

7. 5
   − 4
   ☐

○ 3   ○ 2
● 1   ○ 0

8. Miles found 3 rocks. He gave 1 to his brother. How many rocks does he have left?

○ 5   ○ 4
○ 3   ● 2   STOP

54   Grade 1 • Chapter 2 Subtraction Concepts

Name _____

🖐 **Oral Assessment Response Sheet**

1. _____ **4** _____   2. _____ **3** _____

3. _**7**_, _**4**_, _**3**_   4. _____ **0** _____

   $\frac{7}{} \ominus \frac{4}{} = \frac{3}{}$

5. | **See students' work.** |

6. _____ **5** _____   7. _____ **2** _____

56   Grade 1 • Chapter 2 Subtraction Concepts

Name _____

🖐 **Listening Assessment Response Sheet**

1.

   _**8**_   _**6**_

2.

   _____ **2** _____

3.

   $\frac{9}{} \ominus \frac{3}{} = \frac{6}{}$

4.

   $\frac{6}{} \ominus \frac{1}{} = \frac{5}{}$

5.

   $\frac{9}{} \ominus \frac{4}{} = \frac{5}{}$

6.

   $\frac{8}{} \ominus \frac{7}{} = \frac{1}{}$

7.

   $\frac{9}{} \ominus \frac{4}{} = \frac{5}{}$ | **9** |
                                                      | **4** |
                                                      | **5** |

58   Grade 1 • Chapter 2 Subtraction Concepts

Grade 1 • Chapter 2 Subtraction Concepts   **A12**

Answers (Am I Ready? Practice, Review, Apply, and Diagnostic Test)

Name _____

Am I Ready?

Practice

Add.

1. 5 + 1 = __6__

2. 6 + 4 = __10__

3. 5 + 3 = __8__

4. 9 + 1 = __10__

5. 2 + 7 = __9__

6. 4 + 4 = __8__

7. 5 + 0 = __5__

8. 9 + 3 = __12__

9. 3 + 3 = __6__

Use the pictures to write an addition number sentence.

10.

___4___ (+) ___3___ (=) ___7___

Name _____

Am I Ready?

Review

> **Addition sentences can be written across or up and down.**
>
> ○○ ●●●   2 ○○
> 2 + 3 = __5__   +3 ●●●
>   ‾‾‾
>   5

Add.

1. 4 + 2 = __6__   2. 5 + 3 = __8__

3. 7 + 2 = __9__   4. 3 + 1 = __4__

5. 2   6. 6
   +1   +4
   ‾‾   ‾‾
    3   10

7. 5   8. 9
   +5   +2
   ‾‾   ‾‾
   10   11

9. 4   10. 8
   +5   +3
   ‾‾   ‾‾
    9   11

Name _____

Am I Ready?

Apply

Solve.

1. Ben gave 4 nuts to a squirrel. Ben gave 2 nuts to a chipmunk. How many nuts did Ben give away? __6__ nuts

2. There are 5 spoons in the drawer. There are 4 spoons on the table. How many spoons are there in all? __9__ spoons

3. Maya gave 3 flowers to her aunt. She gave 3 flowers to her uncle. How many flowers did Maya give away? __6__ flowers

4. Ray has 6 baseball cards. Luis has 5 baseball cards. If they put all of their cards together, how many cards will Ray and Luis have? __11__ cards

5. There are 4 lemons on the tree. There are 6 lemons on the ground. How many lemons are there in all? __10__ lemons

---

Name _____

Diagnostic Test

Am I Ready for the Chapter?

1. Circle the addition sign.

   (+)   −   =

2. Circle the equal sign.

   +   −   (=)

Add.

3. 4   4. 1   5. 6
   +4   +5   +4
   ‾‾   ‾‾   ‾‾
    8   6   10

6. 3   7. 1   8. 4
   +2   +4   +2
   ‾‾   ‾‾   ‾‾
    5   5   6

9. 5   10. 0   11. 5
   +3   +3   +5
   ‾‾   ‾‾   ‾‾
    8   3   10

Use the picture to write an addition number sentence.

12.

___5___ (+) ___3___ (=) ___8___

Name _____

Pretest

Use the number line to help you add. Write the sum.

```
0  1  2  3  4  5  6  7  8  9  10 11 12
```

1. $5 + 2 =$ **7** | 2. $7 + 5 =$ **12**

Write the sum.

3. 3
   +3
   ___
    6

4. 3
   +4
   ___
    7

5. Count on to add.

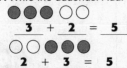

$6 + 2 =$ **8**

6. Make a ten. Write that number. Add the other number to find the sum.

⑥ + ④ + 3 = ___ **13**

   [10]

7. Write the addends. Add.

● ● ● ○ ○

__3__ + __2__ = __5__

○ ○ ○ ● ●

__2__ + __3__ = __5__

Name _____

Check My Progress *(Lessons 1 through 5)*

Circle the greater number. Count on to add.

1. ⑥
   +2
   ___
   [8]

2. ⑤
   +1
   ___
   [6]

3. 1
   +⑦
   ___
   [8]

Use the number line to add.

```
0  1  2  3  4  5  6  7  8  9  10 11 12
```

4. 7
   +4
   ___
   11

5. 6
   +3
   ___
    9

6. 2
   +5
   ___
    7

Write the sum. Circle the doubles facts.

7. $3 + 5 =$ **8**   8. ⊙$8 + 8$⊙ = **16**

9. $6 + 7 =$ **13**   10. ⊙$9 + 9$⊙ = **18**

11. Trinity and Gordon counted spiders. Gordon counted 6 spiders. Together they counted 11 spiders. How many spiders did Trinity count?

   __5__ spiders

Name _____

Vocabulary Test

Use the words in the box. Write your answers.

addends	count on	doubles
doubles minus 1	doubles plus 1	number line

1. A line with number labels is called a ___**number line**___.

2. To add on a number line, start with the greater number and ___**count on**___.

3. Any numbers or quantities being added together are called ___**addends**___.

4. When you add with doubles and add one more, it is called ___**doubles plus 1**___.

5. Two addends that are the same are ___**doubles**___.

6. When you add with doubles and subtract one, it is called ___**doubles minus 1**___.

Answers

Name _____

Chapter Test, Form 1A

Circle the correct answer.

1. Count on to add.

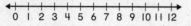

7 + 2 = _____

A. 9   **B.** 10   **C.** 11

2. Circle the greater number. Count on to add.

④ + 2 = _____

F. 2
G. 6
H. 7

Use the number line to add. What is the sum?

3. 8 + 4 = _____

A. 12   **B.** 13   **C.** 14

4. 9 + 3 = _____

F. 10   **G.** 11   **H.** 12

5. Which number sentence matches the picture?

A. 4 + 4 = 8
B. 3 + 3 = 6
C. 2 + 2 = 4

6. Find the sum.

    7
  + 8
  ____

F. 13
G. 14
H. 15

GO on

66   **Grade 1 • Chapter 3** Addition Strategies to 20

Name _____

Chapter Test, Form 1A *(continued)*

Circle the correct answer.

7. Which doubles fact will help you find the sum of 1 + 2?

A. 0 + 0 = 0
B. 1 + 1 = 2
C. 3 + 3 = 6

8. Make a ten to add. Which number is missing?

F. 4   **G.** 5   **H.** 6

9. Which addends match the picture?

_____ + _____ = 8   _____ + _____ = 8

A. 5 + 2; 2 + 5   **B.** 5 + 4; 4 + 5   **C.** 5 + 3; 3 + 5

10. Casey has 3 cans of food for the food drive. Jen has 2 cans of food. Pat has 3 cans of food. How many cans do they have in all?

F. 6
G. 8
H. 9

STOP

Grade 1 • Chapter 3 Addition Strategies to 20   67

Name _____

Chapter Test, Form 1B

Circle the correct answer.

1. Count on to add.

6 + 2 = _____

A. 9   **B.** 8   **C.** 7

2. Circle the greater number. Count on to add.

⑤ + 3 = _____

F. 8   **G.** 6   **H.** 5

Use the number line to add. What is the sum?

3. 6 + 4 = _____

A. 9   **B.** 10   **C.** 11

4. 8 + 2 = _____

F. 12   **G.** 11   **H.** 10

5. Which number sentence matches the picture?

_____

A. 6 + 6 = 12
B. 5 + 5 = 10
C. 4 + 4 = 8

6. Find the sum.

    6
  + 7
  ____

F. 12
G. 13
H. 14

GO on

68   **Grade 1 • Chapter 3** Addition Strategies to 20

Name _____

Chapter Test, Form 1B *(continued)*

Circle the correct answer.

7. Which doubles fact will help you find the sum of 2 + 3?

A. 1 + 1 = 2
B. 2 + 2 = 4
C. 4 + 4 = 8

8. Make a ten to add. Which number is missing?

F. 1   **G.** 2   **H.** 3

9. Which addends match the picture?

_____ + _____ = 7   _____ + _____ = 7

A. 5 + 3; 3 + 5   **B.** 4 + 3; 3 + 4   **C.** 3 + 2; 2 + 3

10. The van has 4 cup holders in the front seat, 4 cup holders in the middle seat, and 3 cup holders in the back seat. How many cup holders in all?

F. 10
G. 11
H. 12

STOP

Grade 1 • Chapter 3 Addition Strategies to 20   69

A15

Grade 1 • Chapter 3 Addition Strategies to 20

Name _____

Chapter Test, Form 2A

Circle the correct answer.

I. Count on to add.

$9 + 3 =$ _____

A. 9   **B.** 10

C. 11   **D.** 12 ⓓ

2. Circle the greater number. Count on to add.

⑥ + 2 = _____

F. 5   **G.** 6

H. 7   **I.** 8 ⓘ

Use the number line to add. What is the sum?

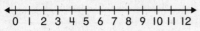

0 1 2 3 4 5 6 7 8 9 10 11 12

3. 7 + 2 = _____

A. 9 ⓐ   **B.** 10

C. 11   **D.** 12

4. 6 + 5 = _____

F. 8   **G.** 9

H. 10   **I.** 11 ⓘ

Find the sum.

5. 7 + 7 = _____

A. 15   **B.** 14 ⓑ

C. 13   **D.** 12

6.   7
   + 8
    ——

F. 15 ⓕ   **G.** 14

H. 13   **I.** 12

GO on

70   **Grade 1 • Chapter 3** Addition Strategies to 20

Name _____

Chapter Test, Form 2A *(continued)*

Write the correct answer.

7. Write a doubles fact that will help you find the sum of 6 + 7.

  6 + **6** = **12**

or 7 + 7 = 14

8. On Monday there were 3 students absent in Miss Cook's class. On Tuesday there were 5 students absent and on Wednesday 4 students were absent. How many students were absent in all?

  12 students

---

9. Make a ten to add. Write the missing numbers.

$$
\begin{array}{r} 8 \\ + 5 \\ \hline \boxed{13} \end{array} \rightarrow \begin{array}{r} 10 \\ + \boxed{3} \\ \hline \boxed{13} \end{array}
$$

10. Make a ten. Write that number. Add the other number to find the sum.

② + ⑧ + 1 = **11**

   10

Grade 1 • Chapter 3 Addition Strategies to 20   71

Name _____

Chapter Test, Form 2B

Circle the correct answer.

I. Count on to add.

$5 + 2 =$ _____

A. 6   **B.** 7 ⓑ

C. 8   **D.** 9

2. Circle the greater number. Count on to add.

⑤ + 3 = _____

F. 5   **G.** 6

H. 7   **I.** 8 ⓘ

Use the number line to add. What is the sum?

0 1 2 3 4 5 6 7 8 9 10 11 12

3. 6 + 3 = _____

A. 9 ⓐ   **B.** 8

C. 7   **D.** 6

4. 9 + 2 = _____

F. 9   **G.** 10

H. 11 ⓗ   **I.** 12

Find the sum.

5. 5 + 5 = _____

A. 12   **B.** 11

C. 10 ⓒ   **D.** 9

6.   5
   + 6
    ——

F. 10   **G.** 11 ⓖ

H. 12   **I.** 13

GO on

72   **Grade 1 • Chapter 3** Addition Strategies to 20

Name _____

Chapter Test, Form 2B *(continued)*

Write the correct answer.

7. Write a doubles fact that will help you find the sum of 8 + 9.

  8 + **8** = **16**

or 9 + 9 = 18

8. Jason ate 7 carrot sticks for lunch on Tuesday. He ate 5 sticks on Wednesday. He ate 4 sticks on Thursday. How many carrot sticks did he eat in all?

  16 carrot sticks

---

9. Make a ten to add. Write the missing numbers.

$$
\begin{array}{r} 8 \\ + 4 \\ \hline \boxed{12} \end{array} \rightarrow \begin{array}{r} 10 \\ + \boxed{2} \\ \hline \boxed{12} \end{array}
$$

10. Make a ten to add. Add the other number to find the sum.

⑦ + ③ + 3 = **13**

   10

Grade 1 • Chapter 3 Addition Strategies to 20   73

Name _____

Chapter Test, Form 3A

Write the correct answer.
Circle the greater number. Count on to add.

1. ⑤+ 2 = **7**   2. ⑧+ 2 = **10**

Use the number line to add. Write the sum.

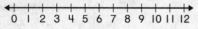

3. 7 + 3 = **10**

4. 9
   + 3
   ‾‾‾
   12

Find the sum.

5. 4 + 4 = **8**

6. 7
   + 8
   ‾‾‾
   15

7. Write a doubles fact that will help you find the sum of 7 + 8.

   7 + **7** = **14**
   or 8 + 8 = 16

8. Make a ten to add. Write the missing numbers.

   7   10
   + 6 → + **3**
   ‾‾‾   ‾‾‾
   13   **13**

GO on

74   Grade 1 • **Chapter 3** Addition Strategies to 20

Name _____

Chapter Test, Form 3A   *(continued)*

Write the correct answer.

9. Write the addends. Add.

   3 + **4** = **7**   **4** + **3** = **7**

10. Make a ten. Write that number. Add the other number to find the sum.

   ⑥+④+ 3 = **13**
     ↘ ↓
     10

Write the addition number sentence and solve.

11. One ladybug has 6 dots. The other ladybug has 3 dots. How many dots do they have altogether?

   6 + **3** = **9** dots

12. 4 frogs jump into the pond. 3 sit on the log. How many frogs are there in all?

   4 + **3** = **7** frogs

13. Ava ate 2 slices of pizza for dinner. She also ate 2 carrots and 1 apple. How many pieces of food did Ava eat in all?

   2 + **2** + **1** = **5**

STOP

Grade 1 • **Chapter 3** Addition Strategies to 20   75

Name _____

Chapter Test, Form 3B

Write the correct answer.
Circle the greater number. Count on to add.

1. 2 +⑥= **8**   2. ③+ 1 = **4**

Use the number line to add. Write the sum.

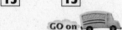

3. 5 + 3 = **8**   4. 6 + 4 = **10**

Write the sum.

5. 6
   + 6
   ‾‾‾
   12

6. 4
   + 5
   ‾‾‾
   9

7. Write a doubles fact that will help you find the sum of 8 + 9.

   8 + **8** = **16**
   or 9 + 9 = 18

8. Make a ten to add. Write the missing numbers.

   8   10
   + 4 → + **2**
   ‾‾‾   ‾‾‾
   12   **12**

GO on

76   Grade 1 • **Chapter 3** Addition Strategies to 20

Name _____

Chapter Test, Form 3B   *(continued)*

Write the correct answer.

9. Write the addends. Add.

   4 + **3** = **7**   **3** + **4** = **7**

10. Add the doubles. Write that number. Add the other number to find the sum.

   ⑥+⑥+ 2 = **14**
     ↘ ↓
     12

Write the addition number sentence and solve.

11. Tom sees 5 red bikes. He sees 2 blue bikes. How many bikes are there in all?

   5 + **2** = **7** bikes

12. 6 children play tag. 3 play hide-and-seek. How many children are playing?

   6 + **3** = **9** children

13. 7 children walked to school. The same number of children rode the bus. How many children are there in all?

   7 + **7** = **14** children

STOP

Grade 1 • **Chapter 3** Addition Strategies to 20   77

A17

Grade 1 • Chapter 3 Addition Strategies to 20

Answers (STP, Oral and Listening Assessment Response Sheet)

Name _____

Standardized Test Practice

Listen as your teacher reads each problem.
Choose the correct answer.

Example A

Start with the greater number. Count on to add.

$4 + 2 =$ _____

○ 4   ○ 5
● 6   ○ 7

Example B

Find the sum.

$4 + 4 =$ _____

○ 7   ○ 9
● 8   ○ 10

---

1. Use the number line to add. What is the sum?

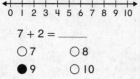

$7 + 2 =$ _____

○ 7   ○ 8
● 9   ○ 10

2. Rose had 5 pennies. She got 2 more. How many pennies does Rose have now?

○ 4   ○ 5
○ 6   ● 7

 GO on

78

Grade 1 • Chapter 3 Addition Strategies to 20

Name _____

Standardized Test Practice *(continued)*

Listen as your teacher reads each problem.
Choose the correct answer.

3. Add.

$5 + 6 =$ _____

● 11   ○ 10
○ 9   ○ 8

4. What is the sum?

$\begin{array}{r} 5 \\ + 5 \\ \hline \end{array}$

○ 0   ● 10
○ 25   ○ 30

---

5. Count on to add.

$4 + 3 =$ _____

○ 4
○ 5
○ 6
● 7

6. Which addends match the picture?

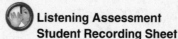

○ 2 + 3; 3 + 2
○ 3 + 4; 4 + 3
○ 4 + 2; 2 + 4
● 5 + 3; 3 + 5

---

7. Make a ten. Add the other number to find the sum.

$5 + 5 + 4 =$ _____

○ 12   ○ 13
● 14   ○ 15

8. Add the doubles. Add the other number to find the sum. What is the sum?

⑥ + ⑥ + 3 = __15__
   ↓   ↓
   [12]

● 15   ○ 13   STOP
○ 11   ○ 9

Grade 1 • Chapter 3 Addition Strategies to 20   79

Name _____

 Oral Assessment
Student Recording Sheet

1. _____ **6 + 2 = 8** _____   2. _____ **7** _____

3. _____ **9** _____   4. **8 shirts**

5. **9 + 2 = 11**

number line 0 to 12

6. _____ **4** _____   7. _____ **10** _____

8. _____ **5 skirts** _____

Grade 1 • Chapter 3 Addition Strategies to 20   81

Name _____

 Listening Assessment
Student Recording Sheet

1. **2** + **5** = **7**   **5** + **2** = **7**

(Yes)   No

2. **9**

3. ○○○○   ○○○
   7

4. **8**
   4 + **5** = **9** or **5** + **4** = **9**

5.
   number line 0 to 12
   8
   8

Grade 1 • Chapter 3 Addition Strategies to 20   83

Grade 1 • Chapter 3 Addition Strategies to 20   **A18**

Answers (Am I Ready? Practice, Review, Apply, and Diagnostic Test)

Am I Ready?

Practice

Name _____

Subtract.

1. 7 − 2 = __5__

2. 8 − 1 = __7__

3. 4 − 0 = __4__

4. 10
    − 5
    ____
     5

5.   6
    − 5
    ____
     1

6.   5
    − 3
    ____
     2

7.   9
    − 7
    ____
     2

8.   7
    − 1
    ____
     6

9.   2
    − 0
    ____
     2

10. Cross out 3 trucks. Use the pictures to write a subtraction number sentence.

__6__ (−) __3__ (=) __3__

Am I Ready?

Review

Name _____

> **You can use a number line to help you subtract.**
>
> 7 − 3 = _____
>
>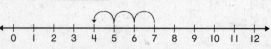
>
> 0 1 2 3 4 5 6 7 8 9 10 11 12
>
> Start at 7 and count back 3.
> You will end up on 4. The answer is 4.
>
> 7 − 3 = __4__

Subtract. Use the number line to count back.

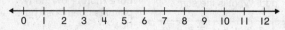

0 1 2 3 4 5 6 7 8 9 10 11 12

1. 5 − 3 = __2__

2. 8 − 2 = __6__

3. 3 − 0 = __3__

4. 10
    − 3
    ____
     7

5.   6
    − 2
    ____
     4

6.   2
    − 1
    ____
     1

Am I Ready?

Apply

Name _____

Write a number sentence to solve.

1. Steve had 8 balloons.
   3 balloons popped.
   How many balloons does Steve have left?

   __8__ (−) __3__ (=) __5__ balloons

2. There are 10 people in the swimming pool.
   6 people get out of the pool.
   How many people are in the pool now?

   __10__ (−) __6__ (=) __4__ people

3. Angela had 7 books.
   She gave 2 books to her sister.
   How many books does Angela have left?

   __7__ (−) __2__ (=) __5__ books

4. There were 4 rabbits in the yard.
   1 rabbit ran away.
   How many rabbits are in the yard now?

   __4__ (−) __1__ (=) __3__ rabbits

Diagnostic Test

Am I Ready for the Chapter?

Name _____

1. Circle the equal sign.

   +   −   ⊜

2. Circle the minus sign.

   +   ⊝   =

Subtract.

3.   5
    − 2
    ____
     3

4.   8
    − 3
    ____
     5

5.   6
    − 5
    ____
     1

6.   4
    − 0
    ____
     4

7.   9
    − 6
    ____
     3

8.   7
    − 5
    ____
     2

9.   2
    − 1
    ____
     1

10. 3
    − 3
    ____
     0

11. 5
    − 4
    ____
     1

Cross out three boats. Use the pictures to write a subtraction number sentence.

12.

__7__ (−) __3__ (=) __4__

Name _____

Pretest

Listen to the directions. Write the answer.

1. Count back to subtract.

   Start with 4.

   4, __3__, __2__

   $4 - 2 =$ __2__

2. Write a number sentence to solve.
   Fran's mother cut 10 pieces of cake.
   There are 2 pieces left over.
   How many pieces of cake were eaten?

   __10__ $\ominus$ __2__ $\equiv$ __8__ pieces

3. Use the number line to help you subtract.

   0 1 2 3 4 5 6 7 8 9 10 11 12

   $11 - 3 =$ __8__

4. Add the doubles fact. Then subtract.

   $4 + 4 =$ __8__ $8 - 4 =$ __4__

5. Add and subtract. Complete the fact family.

   (triangle: 11, 5, 6)

   $6 + 5 =$ __11__ $5 + 6 =$ __11__

   $11 - 6 =$ __5__ $11 - 5 =$ __6__

88   **Grade 1 • Chapter 4** Subtraction Strategies to 20

Name _____

Check My Progress   *(Lessons 1 through 4)*

Count back to subtract.

1.	6	2.	9	3.	10
	-2		-4		-3
	4		**5**		**7**

Use the number line to help you subtract. Write the difference.

0 1 2 3 4 5 6 7 8 9 10 11 12

4.	11	5.	9	6.	8
	-4		-3		-2
	7		**6**		**6**

Add the doubles facts. Then subtract.

7.	5	10	8.	8	16
	$+5$	-5		$+8$	-8
	10	**5**		**16**	**8**

Write a subtraction number sentence to solve.

9. Harrison and his mom baked 12 cookies.
   They ate 4 cookies. How many cookies do
   they have left?

   __12__ $-$ __4__ $=$ __8__ cookies

Grade 1 • Chapter 4 Subtraction Strategies to 20   89

Name _____

Vocabulary Test

Use the words in the box. Write your answers.

count back	fact family	missing addend

1. Addition and subtraction sentences that
   use the same numbers are a __**fact family**__.

2. You can use related facts to find a
   __**missing addend**__.

3. To subtract using a number line, start
   at the greater number and __**count back**__.

Match the picture to its name.

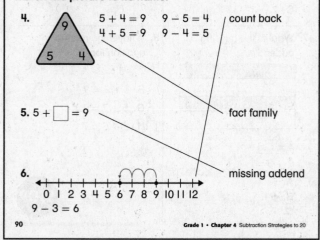

4. (triangle: 9, 5, 4)

   $5 + 4 = 9$ $9 - 5 = 4$ count back
   $4 + 5 = 9$ $9 - 4 = 5$

5. $5 + \square = 9$ fact family

6.   missing addend

   0 1 2 3 4 5 6 7 8 9 10 11 12

   $9 - 3 = 6$

90   **Grade 1 • Chapter 4** Subtraction Strategies to 20

Answers

Answers (Forms 1A and 1B)

Name _____

Chapter Test, Form 1A

Circle the correct answer.

1. Count back to subtract.
   Start with 5.
   5 − 2 = _____
   A. 7   **B.** 3   **C.** 2

2.
   Use the number line to subtract. What is the difference?
   4 − 2 = _____
   F. 6   **G.** 4   **H.** 2

3. Add the doubles fact. Then subtract.

   4 + 4 = 8   8 − 4 = _____
   A. 2   **B.** 3   **C.** 4

4. Take apart the number to make a 10. Then subtract.
   14 − 7
   4 3
   14 − 4 = 10
   10 − 3 = _____
   F. 7   **G.** 6   **H.** 5

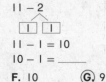
GO on

Grade 1 • **Chapter 4** Subtraction Strategies to 20   91

Name _____

Chapter Test, Form 1A *(continued)*

5. What is the missing addend?

Part	Part
7	_____
Whole	
12	

   7 + ☐ = 12
   12 − 7 = ☐
   A. 5
   B. 6
   C. 7

6. What is the related subtraction fact?
   6 + 2 = 8
   F. 8 − 2 = 6
   G. 10 − 8 = 2
   H. 6 − 2 = 4

7. What is the missing addend?

Part	Part
5	_____
Whole	
10	

   5 + ☐ = 10
   10 − 5 = ☐
   A. 6
   B. 5
   C. 4

8. What is the related addition fact?
   9 − 6 = 3
   F. 9 + 6 = 15
   G. 6 + 3 = 9
   H. 9 + 3 = 12

STOP

92   Grade 1 • **Chapter 4** Subtraction Strategies to 20

Name _____

Chapter Test, Form 1B

Circle the correct answer.

1. Count back to subtract.
   Start with 7.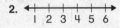
   7 − 3 = _____
   A. 2   **B.** 4   **C.** 6

2.
   Use the number line to subtract. What is the difference?
   6 − 3 = _____
   F. 3   **G.** 5   **H.** 9

3. Add the doubles fact. Then subtract.

   3 + 3 = 6   6 − 3 = _____
   A. 1   **B.** 2   **C.** 3

4. Take apart the number to make a 10. Then subtract.
   11 − 2
   1 1
   11 − 1 = 10
   10 − 1 = _____
   F. 10   **G.** 9   **H.** 8

GO on

Grade 1 • **Chapter 4** Subtraction Strategies to 20   93

Name _____

Chapter Test, Form 1B *(continued)*

5. What is the missing addend?

Part	Part
2	_____
Whole	
9	

   2 + ☐ = 9
   9 − 2 = ☐
   A. 5
   B. 6
   C. 7

6. What is the related subtraction fact?
   5 + 2 = 7
   F. 9 − 7 = 2
   G. 5 − 2 = 3
   H. 7 − 5 = 2

7. What is the missing addend?

Part	Part
3	_____
Whole	
9	

   3 + ☐ = 9
   9 − 3 = ☐
   A. 5
   B. 6
   C. 7

8. What is the related addition fact?
   7 − 5 = 2
   F. 7 + 2 = 9
   G. 5 + 7 = 12
   H. 2 + 5 = 7

STOP

94   Grade 1 • **Chapter 4** Subtraction Strategies to 20

A21   **Grade 1 • Chapter 4** Subtraction Strategies to 20

Name _____

Chapter Test, Form 2A

Circle the correct answer.

1. Count back to subtract. Start with 6.

$6 - 3 =$ _____

(A.) 3   **B.** 2

C. 1   **D.** 0

2. Use the number line to subtract. What is the difference?

0 1 2 3 4 5 6 7 8 9 10 11 12

$12 - 3 =$ _____

F. 5   **G.** 6

H. 7   **(I.)** 9

3. Add the doubles fact. Then subtract.

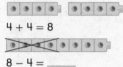

$4 + 4 = 8$

$8 - 4 =$ _____

(A.) 4   **B.** 5

C. 6   **D.** 7

4. Take apart the number to make a 10. Then subtract.

$16 - 9$

6   3

$16 - 6 = 10$

$10 - 3 =$ _____

A. 6   **(B.)** 7

C. 8   **D.** 9

GO on

Name _____

Chapter Test, Form 2A   *(continued)*

Write the correct answer.

5. Find the missing addend.

Part	Part
7	**6**
Whole	
13	

$7 + \boxed{6} = 13$

$13 - 7 = \boxed{6}$

6. Use related facts to add and subtract.

$5 + 9 = \underline{\textbf{14}}$

$14 - 5 = \underline{\textbf{9}}$

7. Subtract. Write an addition fact to check your subtraction.

$15 - 7 = \underline{\textbf{8}}$

$\underline{\textbf{7}} + \underline{\textbf{8}} = \underline{\textbf{15}}$

or 8 + 7 = 15

8. Write a subtraction number sentence. Then write a related addition fact.

Jan had 10 balloons in her hand. 4 balloons blew away. How many balloons does Jan have now?

$\underline{\textbf{10}} - \underline{\textbf{4}} = \underline{\textbf{6}}$

$\underline{\textbf{4}} + \underline{\textbf{6}} = \underline{\textbf{10}}$

or 6 + 4 = 10

 STOP

Name _____

Chapter Test, Form 2B

Circle the correct answer.

1. Count back to subtract. Start with 7.

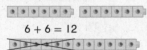

$7 - 2 =$ _____

A. 2   **B.** 3

C. 4   **(D.)** 5

2. Use the number line to subtract. What is the difference?

0 1 2 3 4 5 6 7 8 9 10 11 12

$10 - 2 =$ _____

F. 5   **G.** 6

H. 7   **(I.)** 8

3. Add the doubles fact. Then subtract.

$6 + 6 = 12$

$12 - 6 =$ _____

A. 4   **B.** 5

(C.) 6   **D.** 7

4. Take apart the number to make a 10. Subtract.

$13 - 6$

3   3

$13 - 3 = 10$

$10 - 3 =$ _____

F. 9   **G.** 8

(H.) 7   **I.** 6

GO on

Name _____

Chapter Test, Form 2B   *(continued)*

Write the correct answer.

5. Find the missing addend.

Part	Part
9	**4**
Whole	
13	

$9 + \boxed{4} = 13$

$13 - 9 = \boxed{4}$

6. Use related facts to add and subtract.

$7 + 6 = \underline{\textbf{13}}$

$13 - 7 = \underline{\textbf{6}}$

7. Subtract. Write an addition fact to check your subtraction.

$15 - 6 = \underline{\textbf{9}}$

$\underline{\textbf{6}} + \underline{\textbf{9}} = \underline{\textbf{15}}$

or 9 + 6 = 15

8. Write a subtraction number sentence. Then write a related addition sentence.

Sara had 6 cupcakes. She gave 4 to friends. How many cupcakes does Sara have now?

$\underline{\textbf{6}} - \underline{\textbf{4}} = \underline{\textbf{2}}$

$\underline{\textbf{4}} + \underline{\textbf{2}} = \underline{\textbf{6}}$

or 2 + 4 = 6

 STOP

Name _____

Chapter Test, Form 3A

Write the correct answer.

1. Count back to subtract. Start with 6.

6, __5__, __4__

6 − 2 = __4__

2. Use the number line to subtract. Write the difference.

0 1 2 3 4 5 6 7 8 9 10 11 12

12 − 3 = __9__

3. Add the doubles fact. Then subtract.

8 + 8 = __16__

16 − 8 = __8__

4. Use related facts to add and subtract.

9 + 8 = __17__

17 − 8 = __9__

5. Take apart the number to make a 10. Then subtract.

15 − 6

__1__ __5__ or 5, 1

15 − __5__ = 10

10 − 1 = __9__

6. Complete the fact family.

9 + 2 = __11__   11 − 9 = __2__

2 + 9 = __11__   11 − 2 = __9__

 GO on

Name _____

Chapter Test, Form 3A *(continued)*

7. 8 + 4 = 12. Write a related subtraction fact.

12 ⊖ __8__ ⊜ __4__ or 12 − 4 = 8

8. Complete the fact family.

4 + 7 = ☐   11 − 4 = ☐

7 + 4 = ☐   11 − 7 = ☐

9. Find the missing addend.

Part	Part
9	**4**
Whole	
13	

9 + **4** = 13

13 − 9 = **4**

10. Subtract. Write an addition fact to check your subtraction.

17 − 8 = __9__

__8__ + __9__ = __17__ or 9 + 8 = 17

STOP

Name _____

Chapter Test, Form 3B

Write the correct answer.

1. Count back to subtract. Start with 7.

7, __6__, __5__, __4__

7 − 3 = __4__

2. Use the number line to subtract. Write the difference.

0 1 2 3 4 5 6 7 8 9 10 11 12

11 − 3 = __8__

3. Add the doubles fact. Then subtract.

9 + 9 = __18__

18 − 9 = __9__

4. Use related facts to add and subtract.

8 + 5 = __13__

13 − 8 = __5__

5. Take apart the number to make a 10. Then subtract.

12 − 7

2 **5**

12 − __2__ = 10

10 − 5 = __5__

6. Complete the fact family.

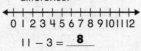

8 + 5 = **13**   13 − 8 = **5**

5 + 8 = **13**   13 − 5 = **8**

 GO on

Name _____

Chapter Test, Form 3B *(continued)*

7. 6 + 5 = 11. Write a related subtraction fact.

11 ⊖ __6__ ⊜ __5__ or 11 − 5 = 6

8.

6 + 9 = **15**   15 − 9 = **6**

9 + 6 = **15**   15 − 6 = **9**

9. Find the missing addends.

Part	Part
4	**9**
Whole	
13	

4 + **9** = 13

13 − 4 = **9**

10. Subtract. Write an addition fact to check your subtraction.

14 − 8 = __6__

__6__ + __8__ = __14__ or 8 + 6 = 14

STOP

Answers (STP, Oral and Listening Assessment Response Sheet)

Name _____

Standardized Test Practice

Listen as your teacher reads each problem.
Choose the correct answer.

Example A

Count back to subtract.
Start with 5.

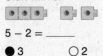

$5 - 2 =$ _____

● 3   ○ 2

○ 1   ○ 0

Example B

Use the number line to subtract. What is the difference?

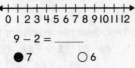

0 1 2 3 4 5 6 7 8 9 10 11 12

$9 - 2 =$ _____

● 7   ○ 6

○ 5   ○ 4

1. Add the doubles fact. Then subtract. Which number shows the difference?

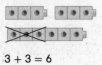

$3 + 3 = 6$

$6 - 3 =$ _____

○ 4   ● 3

○ 2   ○ 1

2. Which subtraction number sentence goes with the story?

Kris sees 7 fish. 6 fish swim away. How many fish are left?

○ $7 - 3 = 4$

● $7 - 6 = 1$

○ $7 - 5 = 2$

○ $6 + 1 = 7$

GO on

Name _____

Standardized Test Practice (continued)

Listen as your teacher reads each problem.
Choose the correct answer.

3. Complete the fact family.

$5 + 4 = \boxed{9}$

$4 + 5 = \boxed{9}$

$9 - 4 = \boxed{5}$

○ $9 - 3 = 6$

○ $9 + 5 = 14$

● $9 - 5 = 4$

○ $9 - 2 = 7$

4. What is the related subtraction fact?

$5 + 2 = 7$

○ $9 - 7 = 2$

○ $9 - 5 = 4$

○ $5 - 2 = 3$

● $7 - 5 = 2$

5. ←|—|—|—|—|—|—|—|—|—|→
1 2 3 4 5 6 7 8 9 10

Use the number line to subtract.

$8 - 3 =$ _____

○ 7   ○ 6

● 5   ○ 4

6. What is the related subtraction fact?

$7 + 7 = 14$

● $14 - 7 = 7$

○ $15 - 9 = 6$

○ $16 - 8 = 8$

○ $17 - 9 = 6$

STOP

Name _____

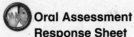 **Oral Assessment Response Sheet**

1. ___10___ ___8___

2. __5__ __3__
   $5 \ominus 3 \ominus 2$

3. __5__ $\ominus$ __2__ $\ominus$ __3__

4.
   __3__ apples

5. __12__ $\ominus$ __3__ $\ominus$ __9__

6. __4__ $\oplus$ __4__ $\ominus$ __8__
   __8__ $\ominus$ __4__ $\ominus$ __4__

7. __11__
   __11__ $\ominus$ __7__ $\ominus$ __4__
   or
   __11__ $\ominus$ __4__ $\ominus$ __7__

8.
   $8 + 2 = \boxed{10}$ $10 - 8 = \boxed{2}$
   $2 + 8 = \boxed{10}$ $10 - 2 = \boxed{8}$

Name _____

 Listening Assessment Response Sheet

1. ▢▢▢▢☒☒
   __6__ $\ominus$ __2__ $\ominus$ __4__

2. ☆☆☆✖✖✖✖✖
   __8__ $\ominus$ __5__ $\ominus$ __3__

3. ←|—|—|—|—|—|—|—|—|—|→
   1 2 3 4 5 6 7 8 9 10
   _____
   $6 - 2 =$ __4__

4. Sample answer: ○○○○○○○○☒
   $9 - 1 =$ __8__

5. The student shows 12 cubes and takes three away. $12 - 3 = 9$

6. The student shows 6 and 6 cubes.   __12__

   The student shows 12 cubes and takes 6 away.   __6__

Answers

Answers (Am I Ready? Practice, Review, Apply, and Diagnostic Test)

Name _____

Am I Ready?

Practice

Circle to make groups of 10.

1.

2.

Write the missing numbers.

3.

1	2	**3**	4	5	6	7	8	9	10
11	12	13	**14**	15	16	17	**18**	19	20
21	**22**	23	24	25	26	27	28	29	**30**

Solve.

4. Each bowl has 10 plums in it. There are 5 bowls on the table. How many plums in all?

   50 plums

Name _____

Am I Ready?

Review

Count ten items. Circle the group of ten.

Circle groups of 10.

1–3. Sample answers provided.

1.

2.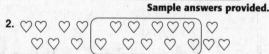

3.

Name _____

Am I Ready?

Solve. Write your answer.

1. Each bowl has 10 apples in it. There are 4 bowls on the table. How many apples are there in all?

   40 apples

2. Each box at the book fair had 10 books in it. 9 boxes of books were sold. How many books were sold?

   90 books

3. Ron has 10 CDs. Sandra has 10 CDs. Ari has 10 CDs. How many CDs do they have altogether?

   30 CDs

4. Kim sorted her marbles into groups of 10. She had 2 groups of 10, plus 5 marbles left over. How many marbles does Kim have in all?

   25 marbles

5. Marc put carrots in bags for snack time. He put 10 carrots in each bag. Marc filled 5 bags and had 3 carrots left over. How many carrots did Marc have in all?

   53 carrots

Name _____

Diagnostic Test

Am I Ready for the Chapter?

Circle to make groups of 10.

Sample answers provided.

1.

Sample answers provided.

2.

3. Write the missing numbers.

1	2	3	**4**	5	6	**7**	8	9	10
11	**12**	**13**	14	**15**	16	17	18	**19**	**20**

Circle groups of 10. Write the number. **Sample answers provided.**

4.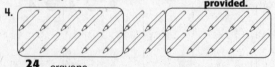

   24 crayons

5. Amy has 3 boxes of crayons. There are 10 crayons in each box. How many crayons does Amy have in all? **30** crayons

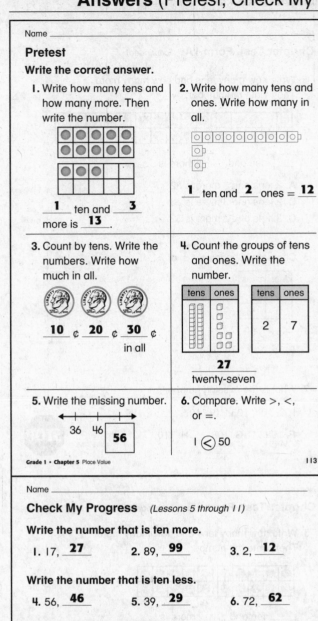

Name _____

Pretest

Write the correct answer.

1. Write how many tens and how many more. Then write the number.

   __1__ ten and __3__ more is __13__.

2. Write how many tens and ones. Write how many in all.

   __1__ ten and __2__ ones = __12__

3. Count by tens. Write the numbers. Write how much in all.

   __10__ ¢ __20__ ¢ __30__ ¢ in all

4. Count the groups of tens and ones. Write the number.

tens	ones
2	7

   __27__
   twenty-seven

5. Write the missing number.

   36   46   **56**

6. Compare. Write >, <, or =.

   1 ⓵ 50

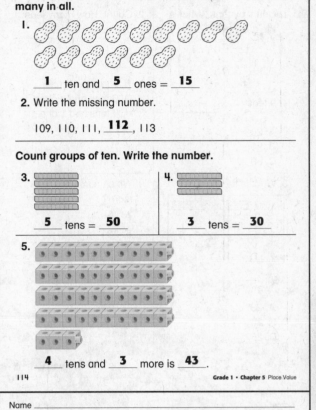

Name _____

Check My Progress   (Lessons 1 through 4)

Write how many tens and ones. Write how many in all.

1.

   __1__ ten and __5__ ones = __15__

2. Write the missing number.

   109, 110, 111, __112__, 113

Count groups of ten. Write the number.

3.

   __5__ tens = __50__

4.

   __3__ tens = __30__

5.

   __4__ tens and __3__ more is __43__.

Name _____

Check My Progress   (Lessons 5 through 11)

Write the number that is ten more.

1. 17, __27__   2. 89, __99__   3. 2, __12__

Write the number that is ten less.

4. 56, __46__   5. 39, __29__   6. 72, __62__

7. Write the missing number.

   97, 98, 99, __100__, 101, 102

8. Count the groups of ten. Write the number.

   __4__ tens = __40__

Write >, <, or =.

9. 21 Ⓢ 19   10. 34 Ⓢ 39

11. 17 ⓔ 17   12. 51 Ⓢ 50

13. Ginny has 24 dolls. How many tens and ones does she have?

    __2__ tens __4__ ones

Name _____

Vocabulary Test

Choose a word from the box to complete each sentence.

equal to (=)	greater than (>)	less than (<)
ones	regroup	tens

1. The numbers in the range of 10 to 99 are __tens__.

2. The number or group with fewer is __less than (<)__.

3. When you take apart a number to write it in a new way, you __regroup__.

4. The numbers in the range of 0 to 9 are __ones__.

5. The number or group with more is __greater than (>)__.

6. __Equal to (=)__ means is the same as.

Name _____

Chapter Test, Form 1A

Circle the correct answer.

1. Count by tens. What is the number?

4 tens = _____
forty

A. 20
B. 40
C. 60

2. Count. How many tens and ones?

F. 1 ten and 4 ones
G. 3 tens and 4 ones
H. 4 tens and 1 one

3. What is the number?

tens	ones	tens	ones
		2	5

twenty-five

A. 23
B. 24
C. 25

4. Which number is ten more?

28, _____

F. 32
G. 38
H. 44

GO on

Name _____

Chapter Test, Form 1A   *(continued)*

5. Write how many tens and how many more. Then write the number.

_____ ten and _____ more is _____.

A. 2 tens and 3 more is 32
B. 2 tens and 3 more is 23
C. 3 tens and 2 more is 32

6. Compare. Choose >, <, or =.

tens	ones
6	5
5	4

65 ◯ 54

F. <   **G.** >   H. =

7. What is the missing number?

103, 104, 105, 106, 107, _____, 109

F. 104   **G.** 108   H. 110

STOP

Name _____

Chapter Test, Form 1B

Circle the correct answer.

1. Count by tens. What is the number?

5 tens = _____
fifty

A. 20
B. 40
C. 50

2. Count. How many tens and ones?

F. 1 ten and 6 ones
G. 7 tens and 1 one
H. 1 ten and 7 ones

3. What is the number?

tens	ones	tens	ones
		3	5

thirty-five

A. 25
B. 35
C. 53

4. Which number is ten less?

_____, 100

F. 80
G. 85
H. 90

GO on

Name _____

Chapter Test, Form 1B   *(continued)*

5. Write how many tens and how many more. Then write the number.

_____ ten and _____ more is _____.

A. 1 ten and 7 more is 17
B. 7 tens and 1 more is 71
C. 1 ten and 7 more is 71

6. Compare. Choose >, <, or =.

tens	ones
3	5
4	6

35 ◯ 46

F. <   G. >   H. =

7. What is the missing number?

115, 116, _____, 118, 119

A. 117   B. 127   C. 128

STOP

Answers (Forms 2A and 2B)

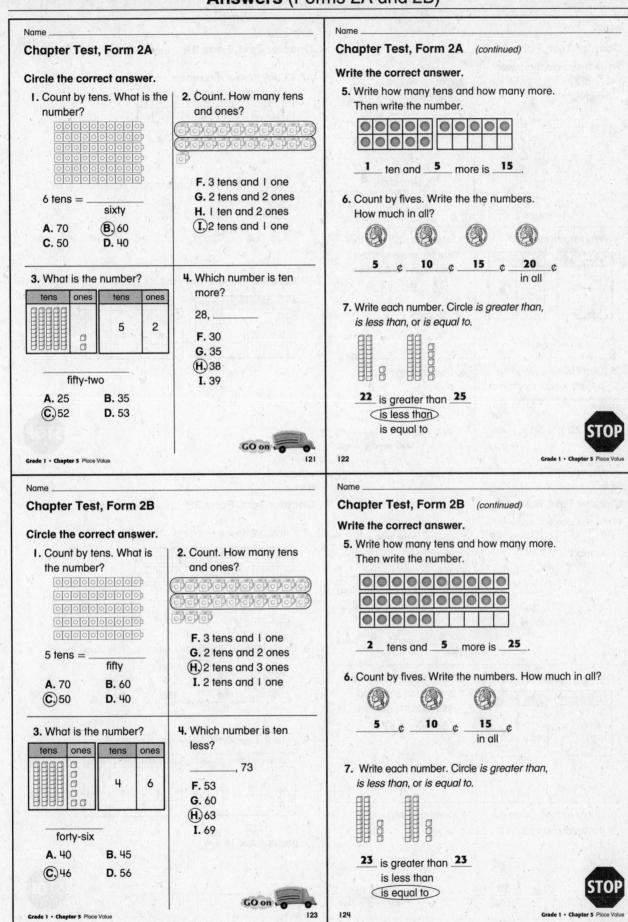

Name _____

Chapter Test, Form 2A

Circle the correct answer.

1. Count by tens. What is the number?

6 tens = _____
sixty

A. 70   **B.** 60
C. 50   D. 40

2. Count. How many tens and ones?

F. 3 tens and 1 one
G. 2 tens and 2 ones
H. 1 ten and 2 ones
I. 2 tens and 1 one

3. What is the number?

tens	ones		tens	ones
			5	2

_____
fifty-two

A. 25   B. 35
C. 52   D. 53

4. Which number is ten more?

28, _____

F. 30
G. 35
H. 38
I. 39

GO on

Grade 1 • Chapter 5 Place Value   121

Name _____

Chapter Test, Form 2A   (continued)

Write the correct answer.

5. Write how many tens and how many more. Then write the number.

__1__ ten and __5__ more is __15__.

6. Count by fives. Write the the numbers. How much in all?

__5__ ¢   __10__ ¢   __15__ ¢   __20__ ¢
in all

7. Write each number. Circle *is greater than*, *is less than*, or *is equal to*.

__22__ is greater than __25__
(is less than)
is equal to

STOP

122   Grade 1 • Chapter 5 Place Value

Name _____

Chapter Test, Form 2B

Circle the correct answer.

1. Count by tens. What is the number?

5 tens = _____
fifty

A. 70   B. 60
C. 50   D. 40

2. Count. How many tens and ones?

F. 3 tens and 1 one
G. 2 tens and 2 ones
H. 2 tens and 3 ones
I. 2 tens and 1 one

3. What is the number?

tens	ones		tens	ones
			4	6

_____
forty-six

A. 40   B. 45
C. 46   D. 56

4. Which number is ten less?

_____, 73

F. 53
G. 60
H. 63
I. 69

GO on

Grade 1 • Chapter 5 Place Value   123

Name _____

Chapter Test, Form 2B   (continued)

Write the correct answer.

5. Write how many tens and how many more. Then write the number.

__2__ tens and __5__ more is __25__.

6. Count by fives. Write the numbers. How much in all?

__5__ ¢   __10__ ¢   __15__ ¢
in all

7. Write each number. Circle *is greater than*, *is less than*, or *is equal to*.

__23__ is greater than __23__
is less than
(is equal to)

STOP

124   Grade 1 • Chapter 5 Place Value

Answers

Grade 1 • Chapter 5 Place Value   **A28**

Answers (Forms 3A and 3B)

Name _____

Chapter Test, Form 3A

Write the correct answer.

1. Count by tens. Write the number.

7 tens = __**70**__
seventy

2. Count. Write the numbers.

__**3**__ tens and __**6**__
more is __**36**__.

3. What is the number?

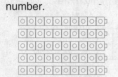

tens	ones
	2 8

__**28**__
twenty-eight

4. Write the numbers that are ten more and ten less than the number.

__**22**__, 32, __**42**__

5. Count by tens. Write the numbers. How much in all?

10 ¢ **20** ¢ **30** ¢ **40** ¢
in all

6. Compare. Write >, <, or =.

43 ⊙> 34

GO on

Name _____

Chapter Test, Form 3A   (continued)

7. Count. Write the numbers.

__**1**__ ten and __**9**__ more is __**19**__.

8. Count by fives. Write the numbers. How much in all?

5 ¢ **10** ¢ **15** ¢ **20** ¢ **25** ¢
in all

9. Write the number in two ways.

hundreds	tens	ones
1	0	6

__**106**__
one hundred six

STOP

Name _____

Chapter Test, Form 3B

Write the correct answer.

1. Count by tens. Write the number.

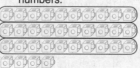

3 tens = __**30**__
thirty

2. Count. Write the numbers.

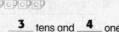

__**3**__ tens and __**4**__ ones

3. Write the numbers.

tens	ones
	3 8

__**38**__
thirty-eight

4. Write the numbers that are ten more and ten less than the number.

__**33**__, 43, __**53**__

5. Count by tens. Write the numbers. How much in all?

10 ¢ **20** ¢ **30** ¢
in all

6. Compare. Write >, <, or =.

45 ⊙< 75

GO on

Name _____

Chapter Test, Form 3B   (continued)

7. Count. Write the numbers.

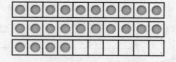

__**2**__ tens and __**4**__ more is __**24**__.

8. Count by fives. Write the numbers. How much in all?

5 ¢ **10** ¢ **15** ¢ **20** ¢
in all

9. Write the number in two ways.

hundreds	tens	ones
1	1	2

__**112**__
one hundred twelve

STOP

A29

Grade 1 • Chapter 5 Place Value

Name _____

Standardized Test Practice

Listen as your teacher reads each problem.
Choose the correct answer.

Example A

Count by tens. What is the number?

2 tens = _____
twenty

● 20   ○ 40
○ 60   ○ 80

Example B

What is the number?

tens	ones

tens	ones
4	3

● 43   ○ 34
○ 25   ○ 24

I. What is the missing number?

75   85   [ ]

○ 86
○ 90
● 95
○ 97

2. Count from 29 to 35. What number comes next?

1	2	3	4	5	6	7	8	9	10
11	12	13	14	15	16	17	18	19	20
21	22	23	24	25	26	27	28	29	30
31	32	33	34	35	36	37	38	39	40

● 36   ○ 29
○ 38   ○ 19

GO on

Grade 1 • Chapter 5 Place Value   129

Name _____

Standardized Test Practice   *(continued)*

Listen as your teacher reads each problem.
Choose the correct answer.

3. Which number is ten more?

24, _____

○ 28   ○ 30
● 34   ○ 38

4. Count by fives. How much in all?

___¢ ___¢ ___¢ ___¢
in all

○ 40¢   ○ 30¢
● 20¢   ○ 15¢

5. Marcy is thinking of a number. It has 8 groups of ten and nine more. What is the number?

○ 69   ○ 79   ● 89   ○ 98

6. What is the number?

hundreds	tens	ones

hundreds	tens	ones

one hundred twenty-four

○ 104   ○ 114
● 124   ○ 142

STOP

130   Grade 1 • Chapter 5 Place Value

Name _____

Oral Assessment Response Sheet

I. _____ 2

2. __3__ tens __4__ ones
34

3. 10¢, 20¢, 30¢, 40¢, 50¢, 60¢

4. 41 and 21

5. The pile of 32 cubes is greater than the pile of 23 cubes.

6. 118 and 98

132   Grade 1 • Chapter 5 Place Value

Name _____

Listening Assessment Response Sheet

I. __3__ tens
30

2. __4__ tens and __2__ ones
42

3. 5¢, 10¢, 15¢, 20¢, 25¢ in all

4. Responses will vary but the first response should be less than 10 and the second response should be greater than 10.

5. 1 hundred, 1 ten, 1 one

134   Grade 1 • Chapter 5 Place Value

Name _____

Am I Ready?

Practice

Write how many tens and ones.

1.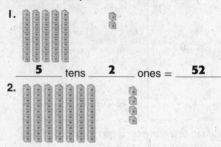

___**5**___ tens ___**2**___ ones = ___**52**___

2.

___**7**___ tens ___**4**___ ones = ___**74**___

Add.

3. $15 + 3 =$ ___**18**___   4. $7 + 4 =$ ___**11**___

Subtract.

5.	8	6.	17	7.	11
	-2		-5		-1
	6		**12**		**10**

8. Pedro painted 17 pictures. He gave 3 pictures to his mom. How many pictures does he have left? ___**14**___ pictures

---

Name _____

Am I Ready?

Review

You can find the difference by counting back.

Find $5 - 3$.
Start at 5. Count back 3.
2
$5 - 3 =$ ___**2**___

Find $8 - 2$.
Start at 8. Count back 2.
7, 6
$8 - 2 =$ ___**6**___

Count back to subtract. Write the difference.

1. $6 - 3 =$ ___**3**___

2. $5 - 1 =$ ___**4**___

3. $8 - 3 =$ ___**5**___

4. $4 - 3 =$ ___**1**___

5. $9 - 3 =$ ___**6**___

6. $7 - 1 =$ ___**6**___

Name _____

Am I Ready?

Apply

Solve.

1. There were 20 rabbits eating carrots. 9 rabbits hopped away. How many rabbits are left? ___**11**___ rabbits

2. 49 people were on a train. 10 people got off. How many people are on the train now? ___**39**___ people

3. Sam had 55 apples. He sold 3 apples. How many apples does Sam have left? ___**52**___ apples

4. There were 99 snowflakes on a window. 50 of the snowflakes melted. How many snowflakes are still on the window? ___**49**___ snowflakes

5. Fatima is reading a book that has 80 pages. She has already read 9 pages. How many pages does Fatima have left to read? ___**71**___ pages

---

Name _____

Diagnostic Test

Am I Ready for the Chapter?

Write how many tens and ones.

1.

___**5**___ tens ___**2**___ ones = ___**52**___

2.

___**4**___ tens ___**7**___ ones = ___**47**___

Add.

3. $5 + 4 =$ ___**9**___   4. $8 + 2 =$ ___**10**___

Subtract.

5.	11	6.	10	7.	12	8.	14
	-5		-3		-6		-4
	6		**7**		**6**		**10**

9. Liz ran 3 miles and walked 1 mile. How many more miles did she run than walk? ___**2**___ miles

A31

Grade 1 • Chapter 6 Two-Digit Addition and Subtraction

Name _____

Pretest

Write the correct answer.

1. 4 tens + 2 tens
= **6** tens

40 + 20 = **60**

2. Count on to add. Write the sum.

47 + 2 = **49**

3. Add.

tens	ones
1	6
+	3
1	**9**

5. Subtract.

6 tens – 1 ten
= **5** tens

60 – 10 = **50**

4. Circle the ones to show regrouping. Write your answer.

15 + 5 = **20**

6. Use the number line to subtract. Circle the number that you land on. Write the difference.

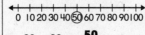

0 10 20 30 40 50 60 70 80 90 100

80 – 30 = **50**

Name _____

Check My Progress   (Lessons 1 through 5)

Count on to add. Write the sum.

1. 1 ten + 7 tens = **8** tens   10 + 70 = **80**

2. 2 tens + 5 tens = **7** tens   20 + 50 = **70**

3.

33 + 5 = **38**

4.

46 + 3 = **49**

Add.

5.

tens	ones
3	3
+	6
3	9

6.

tens	ones
5	2
+	5
5	7

7.

tens	ones
2	5
+	4
2	9

8. Antonio scored 25 points on his video game. Caleb score 34 points. How many points did they score altogether?

59 points

9. Molly helped her mom plant 42 flowers on Saturday. On Sunday, they planted 12 flowers. How many flowers did they plant in all?

54 flowers

Name _____

Vocabulary Test

Use the words in the box. Write your answers.

| add | difference | ones | subtract | sum |

1. The answer to a subtraction problem is called the **difference**.

2. You **add** to find the sum.

3. In the number 64, 4 is in the **ones** place.

4. The answer to an addition problem is called the **sum**.

5. You **subtract** to find the difference.

Chapter Test, Form 1A

Circle the correct answer.

1. Add.

3 tens   30
+ 4 tens   + 40

_____ tens

(A.) 7 tens; 70
B. 6 tens; 60
C. 5 tens; 50

2. Count on to add. What is the sum?

42 + 3 = _____

F. 43   **(G.)** 45   **H.** 49

3. Add.

tens	ones
1	3
+	5

A. 14   **B.** 16   **(C.)** 18

4. What is the answer?

19 + 9 = _____

F. 30   **G.** 29   **(H.)** 28

5. Subtract.

9 tens   90
− 2 tens   − 20

_____ tens

A. 4 tens; 40
B. 6 tens; 60
(C.) 7 tens; 70

142   Grade 1 • **Chapter 6** Two-Digit Addition and Subtraction

Chapter Test, Form 1A (continued)

6. Use the number line to subtract. What is the difference?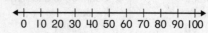

0 10 20 30 40 50 60 70 80 90 100

90 − 40 = _____

F. 40   **(G.)** 50   **H.** 60

7. Use related facts to add and subtract.

10 + _____ = 30
30 − 10 = _____

(A.) 20; 20
B. 15; 15
C. 10; 10

8. Subtract. Which is the related addition fact?

70 − 30 = _____

F. 40 + 20 = 60
G. 30 + 30 = 60
(H.) 30 + 40 = 70

9. Ben has 40 stickers. He gives 30 stickers to his friend. How many stickers does Ben have left?

A. 20
(B.) 10
C. 5

10. There are 30 students in Mrs. Miller's class. 20 of them are girls. How many of them are boys?

(F.) 10
G. 15
H. 20

 STOP

Grade 1 • **Chapter 6** Two-Digit Addition and Subtraction   143

Chapter Test, Form 1B

Circle the correct answer.

1. Add.

6 tens   60
+ 2 tens   + 20

_____ tens

A. 7 tens; 70
(B.) 8 tens; 80
C. 9 tens; 90

2. Count on to add. What is the sum?

33 + 2 = _____

(F.) 35   **G.** 45   **H.** 55

3. Add.

tens	ones
1	7
+	2

A. 20
(B.) 19
C. 18

4. What is the answer?

13 + 7 = _____

(F.) 20   **G.** 29   **H.** 30

5. Subtract.

8 tens   80
− 6 tens   − 60

_____ tens

A. 4 tens; 40
(B.) 2 tens; 20
C. 1 tens; 10

144   Grade 1 • **Chapter 6** Two-Digit Addition and Subtraction

Chapter Test, Form 1B (continued)

6. Use the number line to subtract. What is the difference?

0 10 20 30 40 50 60 70 80 90 100

70 − 20 = _____

F. 30   **G.** 40   **(H.)** 50

7. Use related facts to add and subtract.

50 + _____ = 70
70 − 50 = _____

(A.) 20; 20
B. 15; 15
C. 10; 10

8. Subtract. Which is the related addition fact?

60 − 40 = _____

(F.) 40 + 20 = 60
G. 30 + 30 = 60
H. 30 + 40 = 70

9. Meg had 30 stickers. She gave 20 to her friend. How many stickers does Meg have left?

A. 9
(B.) 10
C. 12

10. There were 50 cups on a table. 20 cups were empty. How many cups were filled?

(F.) 30
G. 40
H. 73

 STOP

Grade 1 • **Chapter 6** Two-Digit Addition and Subtraction   145

A33

Grade 1 • Chapter 6 Two-Digit Addition and Subtraction

Name _____

Chapter Test, Form 2A

Circle the correct answer.

1. Add.

8 tens   80
+ 1 tens + 10
_____ tens ____

A. 5 tens; 50
B. 7 tens; 70
C. 8 tens; 80
(D.) 9 tens; 90

2. Count on to add. What is the sum?

62 + 3 = _____

F. 62   **(G.)** 65
H. 67   I. 69

3. Add.

tens	ones
2	6
+	2

(A.) 28   B. 25
C. 23   D. 21

4. What is the answer?

19 + 4 = _____

tens	ones

F. 33   G. 27
(H.) 23   I. 21

5. Subtract.

6 tens   60
− 3 tens − 30
_____ tens ____

A. 4 tens; 40
(B.) 3 tens; 30
C. 2 tens; 20
D. 1 ten; 10

GO on

146   Grade 1 • **Chapter 6** Two-Digit Addition and Subtraction

---

Name _____

Chapter Test, Form 2A *(continued)*

Write the correct answer.

6. Use the number line to subtract. Circle the number that you land on. What is the difference?

0 10 20 (30) 40 50 60 70 80 90 100

50 − 20 = **30**

7. Use related facts to add and subtract.
20 + **30** = 50
50 − 20 = **30**

8. Subtract. Write a related addition fact.
70 − 30 = **40**
30 + **40** = **70**
or 40 + 30 = 70

9. Write the subtraction number sentence. Then write a related addition fact.

Sam has 80 baseball cards. He gives 20 to his friend. How many cards does Sam have left?

80 − **20** = **60**
20 + **60** = **80**
or 60 + 20 = 80

10. Write the subtraction number sentence. Then write a related addition fact.

Corrie has 40 video games. She gives her brother 10 video games. How many video games does she have now?

40 − **10** = **30**
30 + **10** = **40**
or 10 + 30 = 40

STOP

Grade 1 • **Chapter 6** Two-Digit Addition and Subtraction   147

Name _____

Chapter Test, Form 2B

Circle the correct answer.

1. Add.

6 tens   60
+ 3 tens + 30
_____ tens ____

A. 5 tens; 50
B. 7 tens; 70
C. 8 tens; 80
(D.) 9 tens; 90

2. Count on to add. What is the sum?

53 + 2 = _____

F. 65   **(G.)** 55
H. 52   I. 42

3. Add.

tens	ones
3	4
+	2

A. 26   **(B.)** 36
C. 46   D. 56

4. What is the answer?

24 + 8 = _____

tens	ones

F. 33   **(G.)** 32
H. 23   I. 13

5. Subtract.

5 tens   50
− 1 tens − 10
_____ tens ____

A. 3 tens; 30
(B.) 4 tens; 40
C. 5 tens; 50
D. 6 tens; 60

GO on

148   Grade 1 • **Chapter 6** Two-Digit Addition and Subtraction

---

Name _____

Chapter Test, Form 2B *(continued)*

Write the correct answer.

6. Use the number line to subtract. Circle the number that you land on. What is the difference?

0 (10) 20 30 40 50 60 70 80 90 100

70 − 60 = **10**

7. Use related facts to add and subtract.
50 + **20** = 70
70 − 50 = **20**

8. Subtract. Write a related addition fact.
40 − 30 = **10**
30 + **10** = **40**
or 10 + 30 = 40

9. Write the subtraction number sentence. Then write a related addition fact.

Kim has 50 shells from her trip to the ocean. She brought 20 to school. How many shells does Kim have at home?

50 − **20** = **30**
20 + **30** = **50**
or 30 + 20 = 50

10. Write the subtraction number sentence. Then write a related addition fact.

Jimmy has 50 toy cars. He lost 10 toy cars. How many toy cars does he have now?

50 − **10** = **40**
40 + **10** = **50**
or 10 + 40 = 50

STOP

Grade 1 • **Chapter 6** Two-Digit Addition and Subtraction   149

Grade 1 • Chapter 6 Two-Digit Addition and Subtraction   **A34**

Answers

Name _____

Chapter Test, Form 3A

Write the correct answer.

1. Add.

7 tens	70
+ 2 tens	+ 20
9 tens	**90**

2. Count on to add. Write the sum.

41 + 3 = **44**

3. Add.

tens	ones
4	4
+	5
4	**9**

4. Circle the ones to show regrouping. Write your answer.

25 + 8 = **33**

5. Subtract.

8 tens	80
− 4 tens	− 40
4 tens	**40**

6. Use the number line to subtract. Circle the number that you land on. What is the difference?

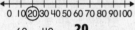

60 − 40 = **20**

GO on

Name _____

Chapter Test, Form 3A *(continued)*

Write the correct answer.

7. Use related facts to add and subtract.

40 + **30** = 70
70 − 40 = **30**

8. Subtract. Write a related addition fact.

70 − 60 = **10**
60 + **10** = **70**
or 10 + 60 = 70

9. Write the subtraction number sentence. Then write a related addition fact.

Jeff caught 70 lightning bugs in a jar. He let 30 out of the jar. How many lightning bugs does Jeff have left?

70 − **30** = **40**
40 + **30** = **70**
or 30 + 40 = 70

10. Write the subtraction number sentence. Then write a related addition fact.

Ricky has 70 baseball cards. He gives 20 cards to his friend. How many cards does Ricky have left?

70 − **20** = **50**
50 + **20** = **70**
or 20 + 50 = 70

STOP

Name _____

Chapter Test, Form 3B

Write the correct answer.

1. Add.

8 tens	80
+ 1 tens	+ 10
9 tens	**90**

2. Count on to add. Write the sum.

53 + 2 = **55**

3. Add.

tens	ones
7	2
+	6
7	**8**

4. Circle the ones to show regrouping. Write your answer.

36 + 7 = **43**

5. Subtract.

4 tens	40
− 1 tens	− 10
3 tens	**30**

6. Use the number line to subtract. Circle the number that you land on. What is the difference?

80 − 20 = **60**

GO on

Name _____

Chapter Test, Form 3B *(continued)*

Write the correct answer.

7. Use related facts to add and subtract.

20 + **60** = 80
80 − 20 = **60**

8. Subtract. Write a related addition fact.

60 − 40 = **20**
40 + **20** = **60**
or 20 + 40 = 60

9. Write the subtraction number sentence. Then write a related addition fact.

Becky saw 50 green beans in her garden. She picked 20 for dinner. How many green beans are still in the garden?

50 − **20** = **30**
20 + **30** = **50**
or 30 + 20 = 50

10. Write the subtraction number sentence. Then write a related addition fact.

In the morning, Carter read 80 pages of his book. In the afternoon, he read 10 more pages. How many more pages did Carter read in the morning?

80 − **10** = **70**
70 + **10** = **80**
or 10 + 70 = 80

STOP

Grade 1 • Chapter 6 Two-Digit Addition and Subtraction

Answers (STP, Oral and Listening Assessment Response Sheet)

Name _____

Standardized Test Practice

Listen as your teacher reads each problem.
Choose the correct answer.

Example A

5 tens + I ten = _____ tens
50 + 10 = _____

- ○ 5 tens; 50
- ● 6 tens; 60
- ○ 7 tens; 70
- ○ 8 tens; 80

Example B

Count on to add. What is the sum?

13 + 3 = _____

- ○ 26
- ● 16
- ○ 15
- ○ 10

I. Add.

tens	ones
I	4
+	3

- ● 17
- ○ 20
- ○ 21
- ○ 27

2. Write your answer.

17 + 5 = _____

tens	ones

- ○ 12
- ● 22
- ○ 19
- ○ 32

GO on

Name _____

Standardized Test Practice *(continued)*

Listen as your teacher reads each problem.
Choose the correct answer.

3. Subtract.

6 tens – 2 tens = _____ tens
60 – 20 = _____

- ○ 3 tens; 30
- ● 4 tens, 40
- ○ 5 tens, 50
- ○ 6 tens, 60

4. Subtract.

9 tens   90
– 2 tens   – 20
_____ tens   _____

- ● 7 tens, 70
- ○ 5 tens, 50
- ○ 2 tens, 20
- ○ I tens, 10

5. Use the number line to subtract. What is the difference?

0 10 20 30 40 50 60 70 80 90 100

60 – 20 = _____

- ○ 10
- ○ 20
- ● 40
- ○ 50

6. Subtract. What is the related addition fact?

80 – 50 = _____

- ○ 50 + 20 = 70
- ○ 20 + 60 = 80
- ● 50 + 30 = 80
- ○ 50 + 40 = 90

STOP

Answers

Name _____

Oral Assessment Response Sheet

I. _____ **9 tens** _____

2. _____ **50** _____

3.

tens	ones
1	5
+	4
1	9

4. _____ **See students' work.** _____

5. _____ **2 tens; 20** _____

6. **Student should circle 10 on the number line; 10**

7. **10 + 30 = 40**
   40 – 10 = 30

8. **30; 50 + 30 = 80 or 30 + 50 = 80**

Name _____

Listening Assessment Response Sheet

I. _____ **40 – 20 = 20** _____

2. _____ **27 + 2 = 29** _____

3. _____ **60** _____

4. _____ **30** _____

5. _____ **21** _____

6. **40; 50 + 40 = 90 or 40 + 50 = 90**

Grade 1 • Chapter 6 Two-Digit Addition and Subtraction

A36

Answers (Am I Ready? Practice, Review, Apply, and Diagnostic Test)

Name _____

Am I Ready?

Practice

Count. Write the number.

1. 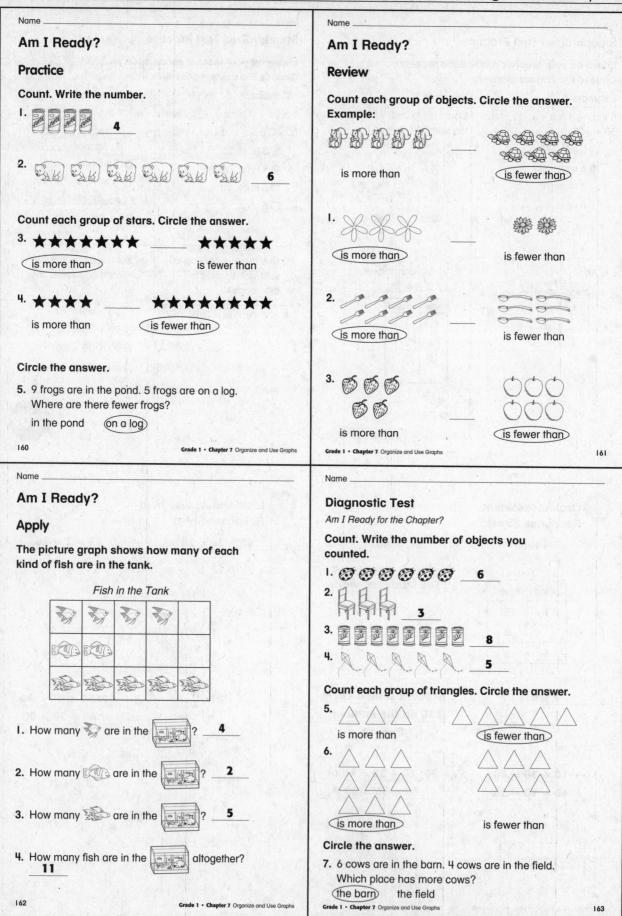 **4**

2. **6**

Count each group of stars. Circle the answer.

3. ★★★★★★★ ____ ★★★★★

(is more than)   is fewer than

4. ★★★★ ____ ★★★★★★★★

is more than   (is fewer than)

Circle the answer.

5. 9 frogs are in the pond. 5 frogs are on a log. Where are there fewer frogs?

in the pond   (on a log)

160   Grade 1 • **Chapter 7** Organize and Use Graphs

Name _____

Am I Ready?

Review

Count each group of objects. Circle the answer.
Example:

____

is more than   (is fewer than)

1. ____

(is more than)   is fewer than

2. ____

(is more than)   is fewer than

3.

is more than   (is fewer than)

Grade 1 • **Chapter 7** Organize and Use Graphs   161

Name _____

Am I Ready?

Apply

The picture graph shows how many of each kind of fish are in the tank.

Fish in the Tank

1. How many are in the ____ ? **4**

2. How many are in the ____ ? **2**

3. How many are in the ____ ? **5**

4. How many fish are in the altogether?
11

162   Grade 1 • **Chapter 7** Organize and Use Graphs

Name _____

Diagnostic Test

Am I Ready for the Chapter?

Count. Write the number of objects you counted.

1. **6**

2. **3**

3. **8**

4. **5**

Count each group of triangles. Circle the answer.

5. △ △ △ ____ △ △ △ △ △

is more than   (is fewer than)

6. △ △ △ / △ △ △ / △ △ ____

(is more than)   is fewer than

Circle the answer.

7. 6 cows are in the barn. 4 cows are in the field. Which place has more cows?

(the barn)   the field

Grade 1 • **Chapter 7** Organize and Use Graphs   163

A37

Grade 1 • Chapter 7 Organize and Use Graphs

Name _____

Pretest

1. How many students ride the 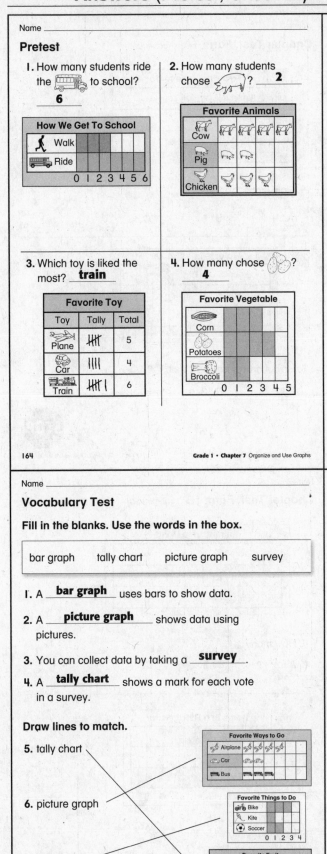 to school?

6

How We Get To School

Walk							
Ride							
	0	1	2	3	4	5	6

2. How many students chose 🐖 ? **2**

Favorite Animals

Cow	🐄	🐄	🐄	🐄
Pig	🐖	🐖		
Chicken	🐔	🐔	🐔	

3. Which toy is liked the most? **train**

Favorite Toy

Toy	Tally	Total
Plane	ЖII	5
Car	IIII	4
Train	ЖI	6

4. How many chose 🥔 ? **4**

Favorite Vegetable

Corn						
Potatoes						
Broccoli						
	0	1	2	3	4	5

164   Grade 1 • Chapter 7 Organize and Use Graphs

Name _____

Check My Progress   *(Lessons 1 through 4)*

The students voted for their favorite fruit. Amie made a tally chart to show how the students voted.

Favorite Fruit

Fruit	Tally	Total
🍇 Grapes	ЖII	5
🍎 Apples	IIII	4
🍊 Oranges	ЖI	6

1. Students should draw 5 grapes, 4 apples, and 6 oranges on the chart.

1. Use the tally chart to make a picture graph.

Favorite Fruit

🍇 Grapes								
🍎 Apples								
🍊 Oranges								

2. Did more students choose apples or oranges? **oranges**

3. How many students chose grapes? **5**

4. Did fewer students choose grapes or apples? **apples**

5. How many more students chose grapes than oranges? **1**

6. How many students were surveyed? **15**

Grade 1 • Chapter 7 Organize and Use Graphs   165

Name _____

Vocabulary Test

Fill in the blanks. Use the words in the box.

| bar graph | tally chart | picture graph | survey |

1. A **bar graph** uses bars to show data.

2. A **picture graph** shows data using pictures.

3. You can collect data by taking a **survey**.

4. A **tally chart** shows a mark for each vote in a survey.

Draw lines to match.

5. tally chart

6. picture graph

7. bar graph

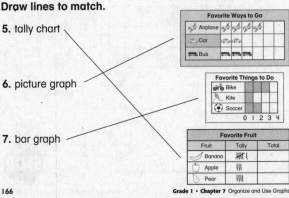

Favorite Ways to Go

Airplane	✈	✈	✈	✈
Car	🚗	🚗		
Bus	🚌	🚌	🚌	

Favorite Things to Do

Bike				
Kite				
Soccer				
	0	1	2	3	4

Favorite Fruit

Fruit	Tally	Total
Banana	ЖI	
Apple	III	
Pear	IIII	

166   Grade 1 • Chapter 7 Organize and Use Graphs

Name _____

Chapter Test, Form 1A

Read the questions. Circle the correct answer.

1. How many ?

Animals in the Zoo

A. 2   **B.** 3   **C.** 4

Favorite Fruit		
Fruit	Tally	Total
Banana	IIII I	
Apple	III	
Pear	IIII	

2. How many votes did the get?

F. 4   **G.** 5   **H.** 6

3. Which fruit has the most votes?

A. apple   **B.** banana   **C.** pear   GO on

Name _____

Chapter Test, Form 1A   (continued)

Favorite Ways to Go					
Airplane					
Car					
Bus					

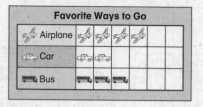

4. How many ?

A. 4   **B.** 5   **C.** 6

Objects in a Drawer					
pencil					
glue					
scissors					
0	1	2	3	4	5

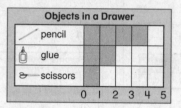

5. How many more ✏ than 🧴?

F. 2   **G.** 3   **H.** 4

STOP

Name _____

Chapter Test, Form 1B

Read the questions. Circle the correct answer.

1. How many 🐔?

Animals on the Farm

Horse				
Turkey				
Sheep				

A. 2   **B.** 3   **C.** 4

Number of Tools		
Tool	Tally	Total
Pail	IIII	
Shovel	II	
Rake	IIII	

2. How many 🪣?

F. 4   **G.** 5   **H.** 6

3. Which item has the most votes?

A. rake   **B.** shovel   **C.** pail   GO on

Name _____

Chapter Test, Form 1B   (continued)

Animals in a Pond					
Duck					
Frog					
Fish					

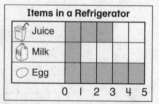

4. How many 🐟?

A. 2   **B.** 3   **C.** 4

Items in a Refrigerator					
Juice					
Milk					
Egg					
0	1	2	3	4	5

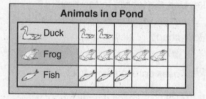

5. How many more ○ than 🧃?

F. 2   **G.** 3   **H.** 4

STOP

A39

Name _____

Chapter Test, Form 2A

Read the questions. Circle the correct answer.

Favorite Foods		
Food	Tally	Total
🍗 Chicken	IIII	
🍕 Pizza	HHT II	
🌭 Hot Dog	HHT I	

I. How many students voted for 🍗?
- **A.** 3
- **(B.)** 4
- **C.** 5
- **D.** 6

2. How many more students voted for 🍕 than 🍗?
- **F.** 6
- **G.** 5
- **H.** 4
- **(I.)** 3

3. How many fewer students voted for 🌭 than 🍕?
- **(A.)** 1
- **B.** 2
- **C.** 3
- **D.** 4

4. How many students voted altogether?
- **F.** 16
- **G.** 18
- **(H.)** 17
- **I.** 19

GO on

Name _____

Chapter Test, Form 2A *(continued)*

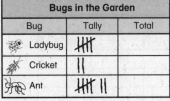

Bugs in the Garden		
Bug	Tally	Total
🐞 Ladybug	HHT	
🦗 Cricket	II	
🐜 Ant	HHT II	

5. Look at the tally chart. Color in the bar graph to show how many of each bug.

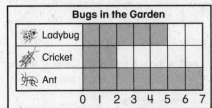

Bugs in the Garden

Ladybug / Cricket / Ant — 0 1 2 3 4 5 6 7

6. Write how many.

____2____ 🦗   ____7____ 🐜   ____5____ 🐞

7. How many more 🐜 are in the garden than 🐞? ____2____

STOP

Name _____

Chapter Test, Form 2B

Read the questions. Circle the correct answer.

Favorite Pets		
Pet	Tally	Total
🐱 Cat	HHT I	
🐶 Dog	IIII	
🐦 Bird	III	

I. How many students chose 🐦?
- **A.** 2
- **(B.)** 3
- **C.** 4
- **D.** 5

2. How many students chose 🐱?
- **F.** 3
- **G.** 4
- **H.** 5
- **(I.)** 6

3. How many fewer students chose 🐶 than 🐱?
- **A.** 1
- **(B.)** 2
- **C.** 3
- **D.** 4

4. How many students were surveyed?
- **F.** 10
- **G.** 11
- **H.** 12
- **(I.)** 13

GO on

Name _____

Chapter Test, Form 2B *(continued)*

Clothes in a Closet		
Clothes	Tally	Total
👖 Pants	II	
👕 Shirt	HHT	
🧥 Jacket	HHT I	

5. Look at the tally chart. Color in the bar graph to show how many of each kind of clothes.

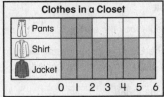

Clothes in a Closet

Pants / Shirt / Jacket — 0 1 2 3 4 5 6

6. Write how many.

____6____ 🧥   ____2____ 👖   ____5____ 👕

7. How many more 🧥 in the closet than 👕? ____1____

STOP

Answers

Answers (Forms 3A and 3B)

Name _____

Chapter Test, Form 3A

Use the tally chart to answer the questions.

Favorite Place		
Place	Tally	Total
🎪 Circus	ⅢⅠ	
🐻 Zoo	Ⅲ Ⅲ	
🎠 Playground	Ⅲ Ⅰ	

1. How many people chose the circus? __**5**__ people

2. How many more people chose the zoo than the playground? __**2**__ people

3. How many people took the survey? __**19**__ people

4. Use the tally chart to make a bar graph. Color in the bar graph to show how many voted for each place.

Favorite Place	
🎪 Circus	
🐻 Zoo	
🎠 Playground	
0 1 2 3 4 5 6 7 8 9	

5. Which place got the most votes?
   zoo

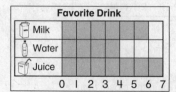

Name _____

Chapter Test, Form 3A *(continued)*

6. Complete the graph.

   Min likes  and ⚽. Ben likes 🚲.
   Jade likes 🪁. Ella likes 🚲 and ⚽.

Favorite Things to Do	
🚲 Bike	
🪁 Kite	
⚽ Soccer	
0 1 2 3 4	

7. How many students voted? __**4**__

8. Which got the most votes? __**riding bikes**__

9. Which got the fewest votes?
   __**flying a kite**__

10. How many fewer votes did 🪁 get
    than 🚲? __**2**__

STOP

Name _____

Chapter Test, Form 3B

Use the tally chart to answer the questions.

Favorite Drink		
Drink	Tally	Total
🥛 Milk	Ⅲ Ⅰ	
💧 Water	ⅠⅠⅠⅠ	
🧃 Juice	Ⅲ ⅠⅠ	

1. How many people chose milk? __**6**__ people

2. How many more people chose juice than water?
   __**3**__ people

3. How many people took the survey? __**17**__ people

4. Use the tally chart to make a bar graph. Color in the bar graph to show how many voted for each drink.

Favorite Drink	
🥛 Milk	
💧 Water	
🧃 Juice	
0 1 2 3 4 5 6 7	

5. Which drink got the most votes?
   juice

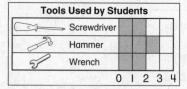

Name _____

Chapter Test, Form 3B *(continued)*

6. Complete the graph.

   Min used a 🔨 and a 🪛. Ben
   used a 🔨 and a 🔧. Jade used a 🔧. Ella
   used a 🔨 and a 🪛.

Tools Used by Students	
🪛 Screwdriver	
🔨 Hammer	
🔧 Wrench	
0 1 2 3 4	

7. How many students voted? __**4**__

8. Which got the most votes? __**hammer**__

9. Which two got the same number of votes?
   __**wrench**__   __**screwdriver**__

10. How many more votes did 🔨 get
    than 🔧? __**1**__

STOP

Answers (STP, Oral and Listening Assessment Response Sheet)

Name _____

Standardized Test Practice

Read the questions. Choose the correct answer.

Example A

Favorite Shape		
Shape	Tally	Total
◯ Circle	‖‖ ‖	
★ Star	‖‖	
△ Triangle	‖‖ ‖	

Look at the tally chart. How many people voted for the △?
- ◯ 7
- ● 6
- ◯ 5
- ◯ 4

1. Use the tally chart to make a picture graph.

Favorite Shape	
◯ Circle	◯◯◯◯◯◯◯
★ Star	★★★★★
△ Triangle	△△△△△△

2. How many students voted for ★?
- ◯ 3
- ◯ 4
- ● 5
- ◯ 6

3. How many more students voted for ◯ than ★?
- ◯ 1
- ● 2
- ◯ 3
- ◯ 4

4. Which shape got the most votes?
- ◯ ★
- ◯ □
- ● ◯
- ◯ △

GO on

Grade 1 • Chapter 7 Organize and Use Graphs   179

Name _____

Standardized Test Practice   *(continued)*

Animals at the Zoo		
Animal	Tally	Total
Leopard	‖‖‖	
Seal	‖‖‖ ‖‖	
Elephant	‖‖‖	

5. How many seals are there?
- ◯ 5
- ◯ 6
- ● 7
- ◯ 8

6. How many fewer votes does leopard have than seal?
- ● 3
- ◯ 4
- ◯ 5
- ◯ 6

Favorite Fruit	
Apple	
Pear	
Banana	
0 1 2 3 4 5	

7. How many more voted for apple than pear?
- ◯ 1
- ● 2
- ◯ 3
- ◯ 4

8. How many total voted for pear and banana?
- ◯ 5
- ◯ 6
- ● 7
- ◯ 8

STOP

180   Grade 1 • Chapter 7 Organize and Use Graphs

Name _____

Oral Assessment Response Sheet

Favorite Pet	
Cat	
Bird	
Dog	
0 1 2 3 4 5 6 7 8	

1. _____ **7**

2. _____ **6**

3. _____ **4**

4. _____ **3**

Favorite Ocean Animal		
Animal	Tally	Total
Whale	‖‖‖ ‖	6
Dolphin	‖‖‖ ‖‖	8
Sea Horse	‖‖	3

182   Grade 1 • Chapter 7 Organize and Use Graphs

Name _____

Listening Assessment Response Sheet

1.

Shapes	
◯ Circle	◯◯◯
□ Square	□□
△ Triangle	△

2.

Silverware	
Spoon	
Fork	
Knife	
0 1 2 3 4 5	

3.

Objects on a Desk		
Object	Tally	Total
Paper Clip	‖‖‖ ‖‖	**7**
Pencil	‖‖‖	**4**
Book	‖‖‖	**5**

184   Grade 1 • Chapter 7 Organize and Use Graphs

Grade 1 • Chapter 7 Organize and Use Graphs   **A42**

Answers

Answers (Am I Ready? Practice, Review, Apply, and Diagnostic Test)

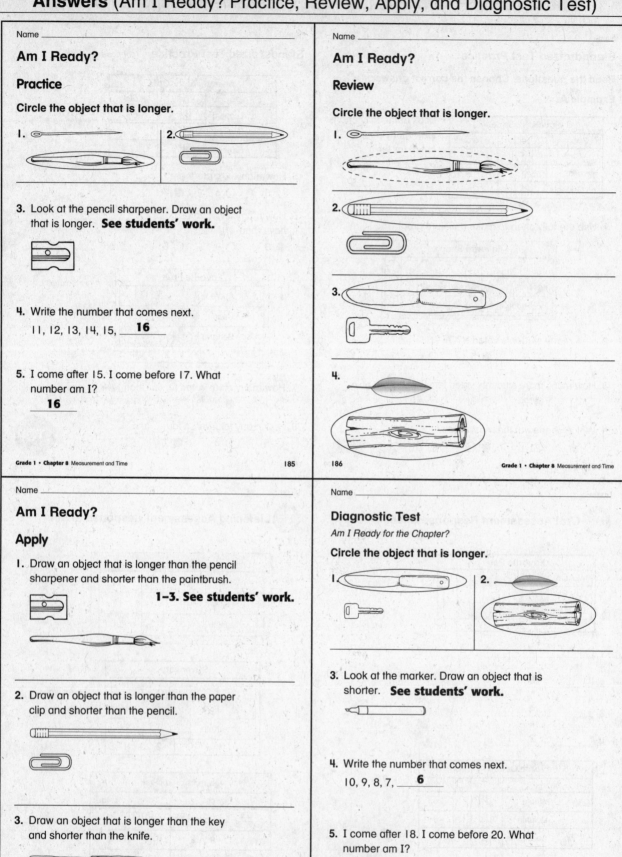

Name _____

Am I Ready?

Practice

Circle the object that is longer.

1.

2.

3. Look at the pencil sharpener. Draw an object that is longer. **See students' work.**

4. Write the number that comes next.
   11, 12, 13, 14, 15, ___**16**___

5. I come after 15. I come before 17. What number am I?
   ___**16**___

Name _____

Am I Ready?

Review

Circle the object that is longer.

1.

2.

3.

4.

Name _____

Am I Ready?

Apply

1. Draw an object that is longer than the pencil sharpener and shorter than the paintbrush.

   1–3. See students' work.

2. Draw an object that is longer than the paper clip and shorter than the pencil.

3. Draw an object that is longer than the key and shorter than the knife.

Name _____

Diagnostic Test

Am I Ready for the Chapter?

Circle the object that is longer.

1.

2.

3. Look at the marker. Draw an object that is shorter. **See students' work.**

4. Write the number that comes next.
   10, 9, 8, 7, ___**6**___

5. I come after 18. I come before 20. What number am I?
   ___**19**___

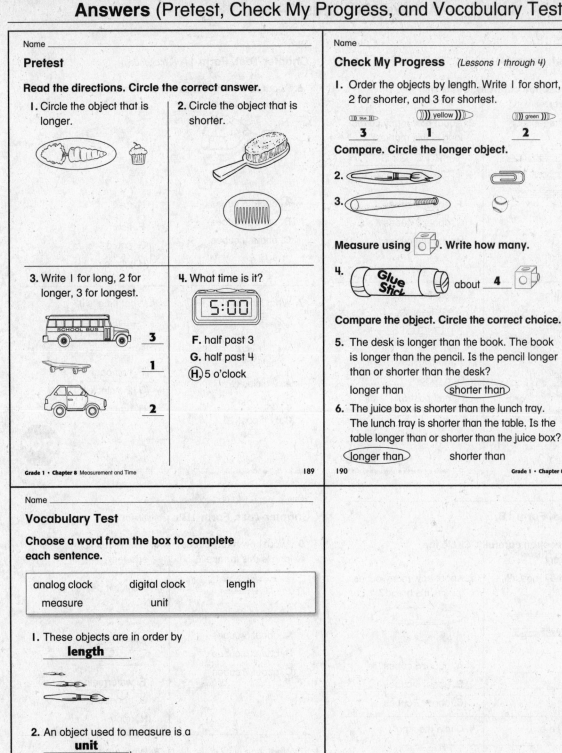

Name _____

Pretest

Read the directions. Circle the correct answer.

1. Circle the object that is longer.

2. Circle the object that is shorter.

3. Write 1 for long, 2 for longer, 3 for longest.

   3

   1

   2

4. What time is it?

   5:00

   F. half past 3
   G. half past 4
   (H.) 5 o'clock

Grade 1 • **Chapter 8** Measurement and Time   189

Name _____

Check My Progress   *(Lessons 1 through 4)*

1. Order the objects by length. Write 1 for short, 2 for shorter, and 3 for shortest.

   blue **3**   yellow **1**   green **2**

Compare. Circle the longer object.

2.

3.

Measure using ▢. Write how many.

4. Glue Stick   about **4**

Compare the object. Circle the correct choice.

5. The desk is longer than the book. The book is longer than the pencil. Is the pencil longer than or shorter than the desk?

   longer than   (shorter than)

6. The juice box is shorter than the lunch tray. The lunch tray is shorter than the table. Is the table longer than or shorter than the juice box?

   (longer than)   shorter than

190   Grade 1 • **Chapter 8** Measurement and Time

Name _____

Vocabulary Test

Choose a word from the box to complete each sentence.

analog clock	digital clock	length
measure	unit	

1. These objects are in order by
   length .

2. An object used to measure is a
   unit .

3. To find the length of a pencil, I can
   measure it.

4. A clock that has an hour hand and a minute hand is an **analog clock** .

5. A clock that uses only numbers to show time is a **digital clock** .

Grade 1 • **Chapter 8** Measurement and Time   191

Answers (Forms 1A and 1B)

Name _____

Chapter Test, Form 1A

Read each question carefully. Circle the correct answer.

1. Which is the longest pencil?

   (A.)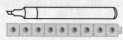
   B.
   C.

2. About how many cubes long is this marker?

   F. about 4 cubes
   (G.) about 9 cubes
   H. about 8 cubes

3. Circle the time.

   A. 11 o'clock
   B. half past 12:00
   (C.) 1 o'clock

4. Circle the time.

    6:30

   F. half past 5
   G. 6 o'clock
   (H.) half past 6

GO on

Name _____

Chapter Test, Form 1A (continued)

5. About how many cubes long is this turtle?

   (A.) about 6 cubes
   B. about 5 cubes
   C. about 4 cubes

6. Which animal is the longest?

   F. fish
   G. squid
   (H.) whale

7. What time is it?

   A. 9 o'clock
   B. half past 9
   (C.) half past 10

8. What time is it?

    2:00

   F. half past 1
   (G.) 2 o'clock
   H. half past 2

STOP

Name _____

Chapter Test, Form 1B

Read each question carefully. Circle the correct answer.

1. Which is the longest?

   A.
   (B.)
   C. yellow crayon

2. About how many cubes long is the bread?

   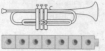

   A. about 5 cubes
   B. about 6 cubes
   (C.) about 7 cubes

3. Circle the time.

   (F.) 3 o'clock
   G. half past 3
   H. 4 o'clock

4. Circle the time.

   3:30

   F. half past 2
   (G.) half past 3
   H. half past 4

GO on

Name _____

Chapter Test, Form 1B (continued)

5. About how many cubes long is this trumpet?

   A. about 5 cubes
   B. about 6 cubes
   (C.) about 7 cubes

6. Which fruit is the shortest?

   F. watermelon
   G. banana
   (H.) apple

7. What time is it?

   A. 10 o'clock
   (B.) half past 11
   C. 12 o'clock

8. What time is it?

    7:00

   (F.) 7 o'clock
   G. half past 7
   H. 8 o'clock

STOP

A45

Grade 1 • Chapter 8 Measurement and Time

Answers (Forms 2A and 2B)

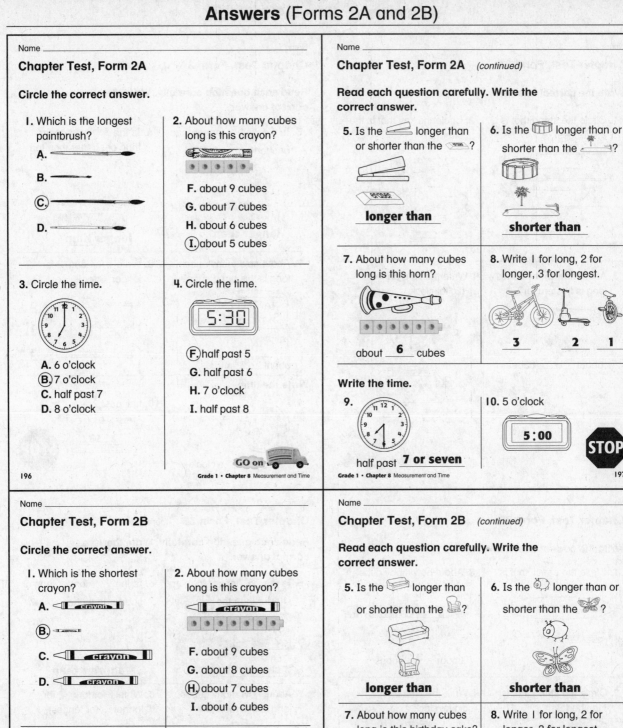

Name _____

Chapter Test, Form 2A

Circle the correct answer.

1. Which is the longest paintbrush?

   A.
   B.
   C.
   D.

2. About how many cubes long is this crayon?

   F. about 9 cubes
   G. about 7 cubes
   H. about 6 cubes
   I. about 5 cubes

3. Circle the time.

   A. 6 o'clock
   B. 7 o'clock
   C. half past 7
   D. 8 o'clock

4. Circle the time.

   5:30

   F. half past 5
   G. half past 6
   H. 7 o'clock
   I. half past 8

Grade 1 • **Chapter 8** Measurement and Time

Name _____

Chapter Test, Form 2A   *(continued)*

Read each question carefully. Write the correct answer.

5. Is the ✂ longer than or shorter than the ▭?

   longer than

6. Is the 🍰 longer than or shorter than the 🌴?

   shorter than

7. About how many cubes long is this horn?

   about **6** cubes

8. Write 1 for long, 2 for longer, 3 for longest.

   3   **2**   **1**

Write the time.

9.

   half past **7 or seven**

10. 5 o'clock

    5:00   STOP

Grade 1 • **Chapter 8** Measurement and Time

Name _____

Chapter Test, Form 2B

Circle the correct answer.

1. Which is the shortest crayon?

   A. crayon
   B.
   C. crayon
   D. crayon

2. About how many cubes long is this crayon?

   F. about 9 cubes
   G. about 8 cubes
   H. about 7 cubes
   I. about 6 cubes

3. Circle the time.

   A. half past 10
   B. 11 o'clock
   C. half past 11
   D. half past 12

4. Circle the time.

   9:00

   F. half past 8
   G. 9 o'clock
   H. half past 9
   I. 10 o'clock

Grade 1 • **Chapter 8** Measurement and Time

Name _____

Chapter Test, Form 2B   *(continued)*

Read each question carefully. Write the correct answer.

5. Is the 🛋 longer than or shorter than the 🪑?

   longer than

6. Is the 🐑 longer than or shorter than the 🦋?

   shorter than

7. About how many cubes long is this birthday cake?

   about **4** cubes

8. Write 1 for long, 2 for longer, 3 for longest.

   2   **3**   **1**

Write the time.

9.

   half past **12**

10. half past 6

    6:30   STOP

Grade 1 • **Chapter 8** Measurement and Time

Grade 1 • Chapter 8 Measurement and Time

A46

Answers

Answers (Forms 3A and 3B)

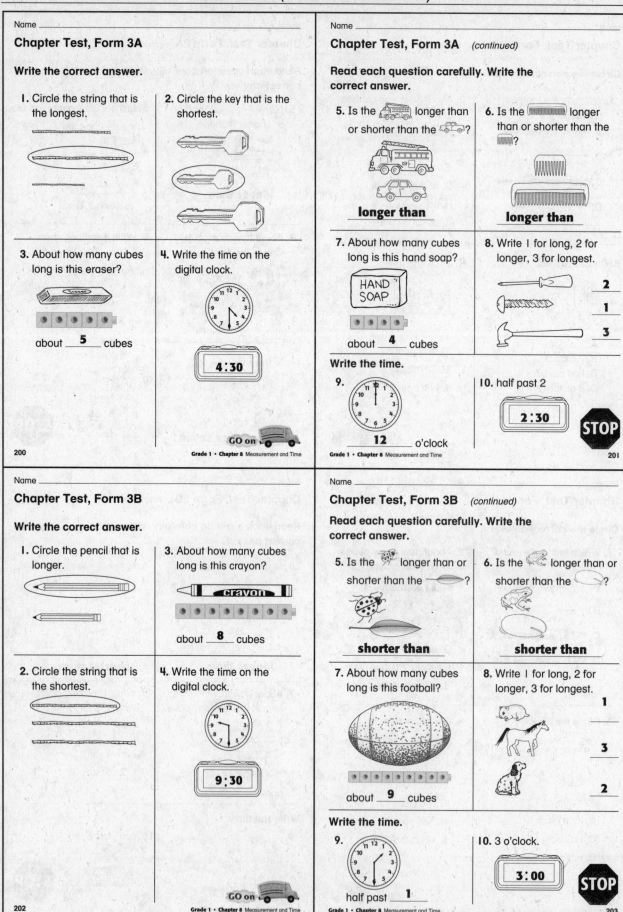

Name _____

Chapter Test, Form 3A

Write the correct answer.

I. Circle the string that is the longest.

2. Circle the key that is the shortest.

3. About how many cubes long is this eraser?

about **5** cubes

4. Write the time on the digital clock.

4:30

GO on

200   Grade 1 • **Chapter 8** Measurement and Time

Name _____

Chapter Test, Form 3A   (continued)

Read each question carefully. Write the correct answer.

5. Is the 🚒 longer than or shorter than the 🚗?

longer than

6. Is the ▭ longer than or shorter than the ▭?

longer than

7. About how many cubes long is this hand soap?

HAND SOAP

about **4** cubes

8. Write I for long, 2 for longer, 3 for longest.

2

1

3

Write the time.

9.

12 o'clock

10. half past 2

2:30   STOP

Grade 1 • **Chapter 8** Measurement and Time   201

Name _____

Chapter Test, Form 3B

Write the correct answer.

I. Circle the pencil that is longer.

3. About how many cubes long is this crayon?

crayon

about **8** cubes

2. Circle the string that is the shortest.

4. Write the time on the digital clock.

9:30

GO on

202   Grade 1 • **Chapter 8** Measurement and Time

Name _____

Chapter Test, Form 3B   (continued)

Read each question carefully. Write the correct answer.

5. Is the 🐞 longer than or shorter than the ▭?

shorter than

6. Is the 🐸 longer than or shorter than the ⬭?

shorter than

7. About how many cubes long is this football?

about **9** cubes

8. Write I for long, 2 for longer, 3 for longest.

1

3

2

Write the time.

9.

half past **1**

10. 3 o'clock.

3:00   STOP

Grade 1 • **Chapter 8** Measurement and Time   203

A47   Grade 1 • **Chapter 8** Measurement and Time

Name _____

Standardized Test Practice

Listen as your teacher reads each problem.
Choose the correct answer.

Example A

Which ribbon is the longest?

○

○

● (longest ribbon)

Example B

Which toy is the shortest?

○ airplane

○ train

● car

I. What time is it?

(clock showing half past 10)

○ 10 o'clock

● half past 10

○ 11 o'clock

2. What time is it?

2:00

○ 1 o'clock

○ half past 1

● 2 o'clock

GO on

204

Grade 1 • **Chapter 8** Measurement and Time

Name _____

Standardized Test Practice (continued)

Listen as your teacher reads each problem.
Choose the correct answer.

3. About how many cubes long is the pencil?

○ about 7 cubes

● about 8 cubes

○ about 9 cubes

4. Which fish is the shortest?

○

○

● (smallest fish)

---

5. What time is it?

(clock showing 7 o'clock)

○ 6 o'clock

● 7 o'clock

○ half past 7

6. What time is it?

9:30

● half past 9

○ 9 o'clock

○ half past 8

STOP

Grade 1 • **Chapter 8** Measurement and Time

205

Answers

Name _____

Oral Assessment Response Sheet

I. **about 6 cubes**

2. **the pencil**

3. **1** o'clock

4. (clock showing half past 12)

5. 2:00

6. 2:30

Grade 1 • **Chapter 8** Measurement and Time

207

Name _____

Listening Assessment Response Sheet

I. Draw your line here.

about **See students' work.** cubes

2. Write your answer here.

See students' work.

3. **See students' work.**

about _____ cubes

4. **See students' work.**

5. **See students' work.**

Grade 1 • **Chapter 8** Measurement and Time

209

Grade 1 • **Chapter 8** Measurement and Time

A48

Answers (Am I Ready? Practice, Review, Apply, and Diagnostic Test)

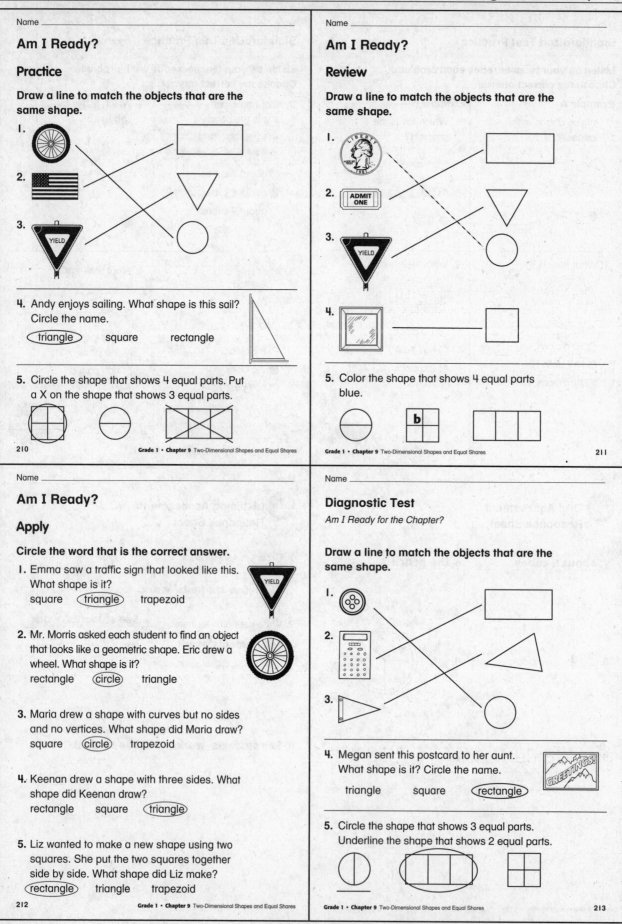

Name

Am I Ready?

Practice

Draw a line to match the objects that are the same shape.

1.

2.

3.

4. Andy enjoys sailing. What shape is this sail? Circle the name.

(triangle)   square   rectangle

5. Circle the shape that shows 4 equal parts. Put a X on the shape that shows 3 equal parts.

210   **Grade 1 • Chapter 9** Two-Dimensional Shapes and Equal Shares

Name

Am I Ready?

Review

Draw a line to match the objects that are the same shape.

1.

2.

3.

4.

5. Color the shape that shows 4 equal parts blue.

Grade 1 • Chapter 9 Two-Dimensional Shapes and Equal Shares   211

Name

Am I Ready?

Apply

Circle the word that is the correct answer.

1. Emma saw a traffic sign that looked like this. What shape is it?
   square   (triangle)   trapezoid

2. Mr. Morris asked each student to find an object that looks like a geometric shape. Eric drew a wheel. What shape is it?
   rectangle   (circle)   triangle

3. Maria drew a shape with curves but no sides and no vertices. What shape did Maria draw?
   square   (circle)   trapezoid

4. Keenan drew a shape with three sides. What shape did Keenan draw?
   rectangle   square   (triangle)

5. Liz wanted to make a new shape using two squares. She put the two squares together side by side. What shape did Liz make?
   (rectangle)   triangle   trapezoid

212   **Grade 1 • Chapter 9** Two-Dimensional Shapes and Equal Shares

Name

Diagnostic Test

Am I Ready for the Chapter?

Draw a line to match the objects that are the same shape.

1.

2.

3.

4. Megan sent this postcard to her aunt. What shape is it? Circle the name.

   triangle   square   (rectangle)

5. Circle the shape that shows 3 equal parts. Underline the shape that shows 2 equal parts.

Grade 1 • Chapter 9 Two-Dimensional Shapes and Equal Shares   213

A49

Grade 1 • Chapter 9 Two-Dimensional Shapes and Equal Shares

Name _____

Pretest

Write the correct answer.

1. Circle the square.

2. Circle the triangle.

Write how many sides and vertices.

3.

__3__ sides
__3__ vertices

4.

__4__ sides
__4__ vertices

5. Write how many equal parts.

__2__ equal parts

6. Write how many equal parts.

__4__ equal parts

214   **Grade 1 • Chapter 9** Two-Dimensional Shapes and Equal Shares

---

Name _____

Check My Progress   (Lessons 1 through 4)

Color the shapes that match the rule.

1. 4 sides

2. 0 vertices

3. 3 sides

4. squares

Write how many.

5.

__3__ sides
__3__ vertices

6.

__4__ sides
__4__ vertices

7.

__0__ sides
__0__ vertices

8.

__4__ sides
__4__ vertices

9. Kaylee has a shape with 3 sides and 3 vertices. Brayden has a shape with 4 sides of equal length and 4 vertices. Name the two shapes. Kaylee has a __triangle__. Brayden has a __square__.

Grade 1 • Chapter 9 Two-Dimensional Shapes and Equal Shares   215

Name _____

Check My Progress   (Lessons 5 through 7)

Color all the closed shapes.

1.

Circle the pattern blocks used to make the shape.

2.

3.

4.

216   **Grade 1 • Chapter 9** Two-Dimensional Shapes and Equal Shares

---

Name _____

Vocabulary Test

Match the two-dimensional shape to its name.

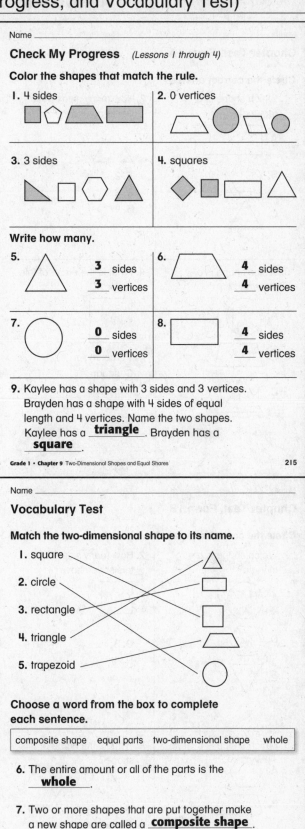

1. square

2. circle

3. rectangle

4. triangle

5. trapezoid

Choose a word from the box to complete each sentence.

| composite shape | equal parts | two-dimensional shape | whole |

6. The entire amount or all of the parts is the __whole__.

7. Two or more shapes that are put together make a new shape are called a __composite shape__.

8. Parts of a whole that have the same size are called __equal parts__.

9. A flat shape, such as a circle, a triangle, or a square is a __two-dimensional shape__.

Grade 1 • Chapter 9 Two-Dimensional Shapes and Equal Shares   217

Answers

Answers (Forms 1A and 1B)

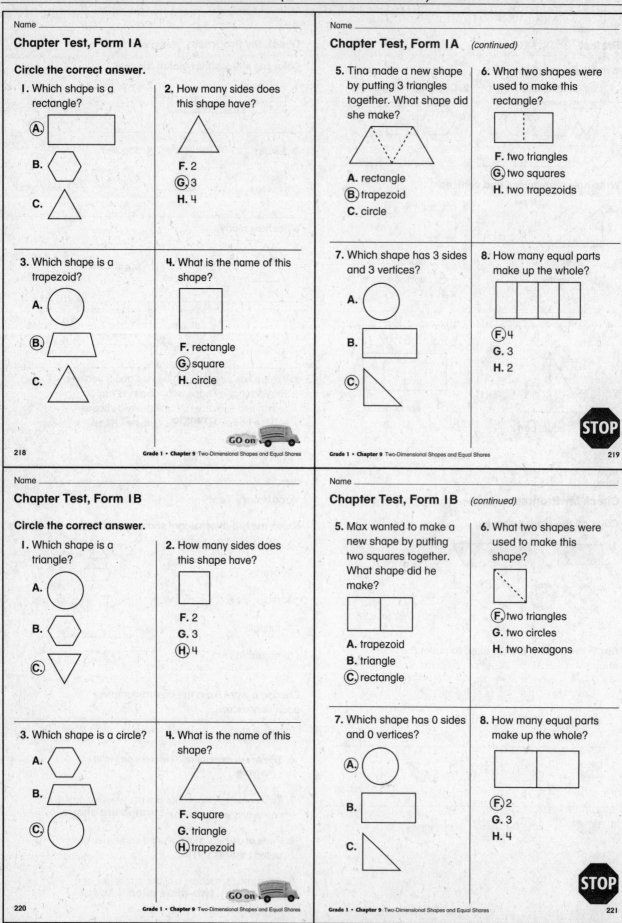

Name _____

Chapter Test, Form 1A

Circle the correct answer.

1. Which shape is a rectangle?

   Ⓐ. [rectangle]

   B. [hexagon]

   C. [triangle]

2. How many sides does this shape have?

   [triangle]

   F. 2
   Ⓖ. 3
   H. 4

3. Which shape is a trapezoid?

   A. [circle]

   Ⓑ. [trapezoid]

   C. [triangle]

4. What is the name of this shape?

   [square]

   F. rectangle
   Ⓖ. square
   H. circle

Name _____

Chapter Test, Form 1A *(continued)*

5. Tina made a new shape by putting 3 triangles together. What shape did she make?

   [trapezoid]

   A. rectangle
   Ⓑ. trapezoid
   C. circle

6. What two shapes were used to make this rectangle?

   [rectangle]

   F. two triangles
   Ⓖ. two squares
   H. two trapezoids

7. Which shape has 3 sides and 3 vertices?

   A. [circle]

   B. [rectangle]

   Ⓒ. [triangle]

8. How many equal parts make up the whole?

   [rectangle divided into 4 parts]

   Ⓕ. 4
   G. 3
   H. 2

STOP

Name _____

Chapter Test, Form 1B

Circle the correct answer.

1. Which shape is a triangle?

   A. [circle]

   B. [hexagon]

   Ⓒ. [triangle]

2. How many sides does this shape have?

   [square]

   F. 2
   G. 3
   Ⓗ. 4

3. Which shape is a circle?

   A. [hexagon]

   B. [trapezoid]

   Ⓒ. [circle]

4. What is the name of this shape?

   [trapezoid]

   F. square
   G. triangle
   Ⓗ. trapezoid

Name _____

Chapter Test, Form 1B *(continued)*

5. Max wanted to make a new shape by putting two squares together. What shape did he make?

   [rectangle]

   A. trapezoid
   B. triangle
   Ⓒ. rectangle

6. What two shapes were used to make this shape?

   [square with diagonal]

   Ⓕ. two triangles
   G. two circles
   H. two hexagons

7. Which shape has 0 sides and 0 vertices?

   Ⓐ. [circle]

   B. [rectangle]

   C. [triangle]

8. How many equal parts make up the whole?

   [rectangle divided into 2 parts]

   Ⓕ. 2
   G. 3
   H. 4

STOP

Answers (Forms 2A and 2B)

Name _____

Chapter Test, Form 2A

Circle the correct answer.

1. What is the name of this shape?

   A. rectangle *(circled)*
   B. trapezoid
   C. triangle
   D. square

2. How many sides does this shape have?

   F. 0
   G. 2
   H. 4 *(circled)*
   I. 6

3. How many sides and vertices does the square have?

   A. 3 sides and 3 vertices
   B. 3 sides and 4 vertices
   C. 4 sides and 4 vertices *(circled)*
   D. 0 sides and 0 vertices

4. How many sides and vertices does a circle have?

   F. 2 sides and 2 vertices
   G. 4 sides and 4 vertices
   H. 3 sides and 3 vertices
   I. 0 sides and 0 vertices *(circled)*

GO on

Name _____

Chapter Test, Form 2A *(continued)*

Circle the correct answer.

5. What two shapes were used to make this rectangle?

   two trapezoids
   two squares *(circled)*

6. Carlos put together the three shapes shown. Circle the new shape he made.

   trapezoid *(circled)*
   circle

7. Which shape shows 2 equal parts?

   A.
   B.
   C. *(circled)*

8. How many parts are shaded?

   $\underline{\quad1\quad}$ of $\underline{\quad4\quad}$ parts

STOP

Name _____

Chapter Test, Form 2B

Circle the correct answer.

1. What shape is this?

   A. rectangle
   B. trapezoid
   C. triangle *(circled)*
   D. square

2. How many sides does this shape have?

   F. 0
   G. 4 *(circled)*
   H. 5
   I. 6

3. How many sides and vertices does the triangle have?

   A. 3 sides and 2 vertices
   B. 3 sides and 3 vertices *(circled)*
   C. 4 sides and 4 vertices
   D. 2 sides and 3 vertices

4. How many sides and vertices does a trapezoid have?

   F. 2 sides and 4 vertices
   G. 0 sides and 0 vertices
   H. 3 sides and 3 vertices
   I. 4 sides and 4 vertices *(circled)*

GO on

Name _____

Chapter Test, Form 2B *(continued)*

Circle the correct answer.

5. What two shapes were used to make this square?

   two triangles *(circled)*
   two rectangles

6. Hannah joined two shapes. She made the following shape. What two shapes did Hannah join together?

   two trapezoids *(circled)*
   two triangles

7. Draw lines to show 4 equal parts.

8. Write how many parts are shaded.

   $\underline{\quad1\quad}$ of $\underline{\quad2\quad}$ parts

STOP

Answers *(side tab)*

Answers (Forms 3A and 3B)

Name _____

Chapter Test, Form 3A

1. Circle the name of this shape.

(triangle)   square

2. How many sides and vertices does this shape have?

__4__ sides __4__ vertices

3. Write how many sides and vertices the circle has.

__0__ sides __0__ vertices

4. Circle the two-dimensional shape this object looks like?

trapezoid   (rectangle)

5. Which shape below has 3 sides and 3 vertices? Circle the name.

square   (triangle)   circle

GO on

Name _____

Chapter Test, Form 3A (continued)

Circle the correct answer.

6. Abbi made a new shape by putting three triangles together. What shape did she make?

(trapezoid)   triangle

7. Carol made a new shape. What shapes did Carol use to make the new shape?

(triangles)   circles

8. Brandon saw a shape with 3 sides and 3 vertices. Did Brandon see a circle, a triangle, or a square?

__triangle__

9. Donna drew a shape with 0 sides and 0 vertices. Did Dona draw a circle, a triangle, or a square?

__circle__

10. Circle the pattern blocks used to make the shape.

11. Draw lines to show 4 equal parts.

STOP

Name _____

Chapter Test, Form 3B

1. Circle the name of this shape.

square   (rectangle)

2. How many sides and vertices does this shape have?

__4__ sides __4__ vertices

3. Write how many sides and vertices.

__3__ sides __3__ vertices

4. Circle the two-dimensional shape this object looks like.

(circle)   trapezoid

5. Which shape below has 4 sides and 4 vertices? Circle the name.

(trapezoid)   triangle   circle

GO on

Name _____

Chapter Test, Form 3B (continued)

Circle the correct answer.

6. Jaden made a new shape by putting 2 triangles together. What new shape did Jaden make?

(square)   rectangle

7. Adam made a new shape. What shapes did he use to make the shape?

rectangles   (squares)

8. Tamika saw a shape with 4 sides and 4 vertices. Did she see a circle, a triangle, or a square?

__square__

9. Guy drew a shape with 3 sides and 3 vertices. Did he draw a circle, a triangle, or a square?

__triangle__

10. Circle the pattern blocks used to make the shape.

11. Draw lines to show 2 equal parts.

STOP

Grade 1 • Chapter 9 Two-Dimensional Shapes and Equal Shares

Name _____

Standardized Test Practice

Listen as your teacher reads each problem.
Choose the correct answer.

Example A

Which shape is a square?

○ (circle)
● (square)
○ (circle)
○ (trapezoid)

Example B

Which shape is a trapezoid?

○ (circle)
○ (square)
○ (circle)
● (trapezoid)

1. How many sides and vertices does a circle have?

● 0 sides and 0 vertices
○ 3 sides and 3 vertices
○ 4 sides and 4 vertices
○ 4 sides and 2 vertices

2. How many sides and vertices does a rectangle have?

○ 0 sides and 0 vertices
○ 3 sides and 3 vertices
● 4 sides and 4 vertices
○ 4 sides and 0 vertices

GO on

230   **Grade 1 • Chapter 9** Two-Dimensional Shapes and Equal Shares

---

Name _____

Standardized Test Practice   (continued)

Listen as your teacher reads each problem.
Choose the correct answer.

3. Which pattern block was used to make the shape.

○
●

4. How many equal parts make up the whole?

○ 6
● 4
○ 3
○ 2

5. How many sides and vertices?

○ 2 sides and 2 vertices
● 3 sides and 3 vertices
○ 4 sides and 2 vertices
○ 4 sides and 4 vertices

6. What shapes were used to make this rectangle?

● squares
○ rectangles
○ triangles
○ trapezoids

STOP

Grade 1 • Chapter 9 Two-Dimensional Shapes and Equal Shares   231

Name _____

Oral Assessment Response Sheet

1. _Students should point to the triangle._

2. _The square and triangle have sides and vertices._

3. Alike: **Both shapes have four sides and four vertices.**

Different: **The square has four equal sides and the rectangle has two short sides and two long sides.**

4.   **4; trapezoid**

5. **3 sides, 3 vertices; student should describe or show how to make a square.**

6.   **6**

7. **Sample answer:**

Grade 1 • Chapter 9 Two-Dimensional Shapes and Equal Shares   233

Name _____

Listening Assessment Response Sheet

1.   **3** sides   **3** vertices

2.   **4** sides   **4** vertices

3. Sample answer: Circles are round, but have no sides or vertices.

4. Alike: Possible responses: Both shapes have 4 sides and 4 vertices.

Different: Possible responses: The square has four equal sides. The rectangle has 2 long sides and 2 short sides.

5. 4 sides and 4 vertices

6. Responses will vary. Possible response:

7. Responses will vary.

Grade 1 • Chapter 9 Two-Dimensional Shapes and Equal Shares   235

Answers

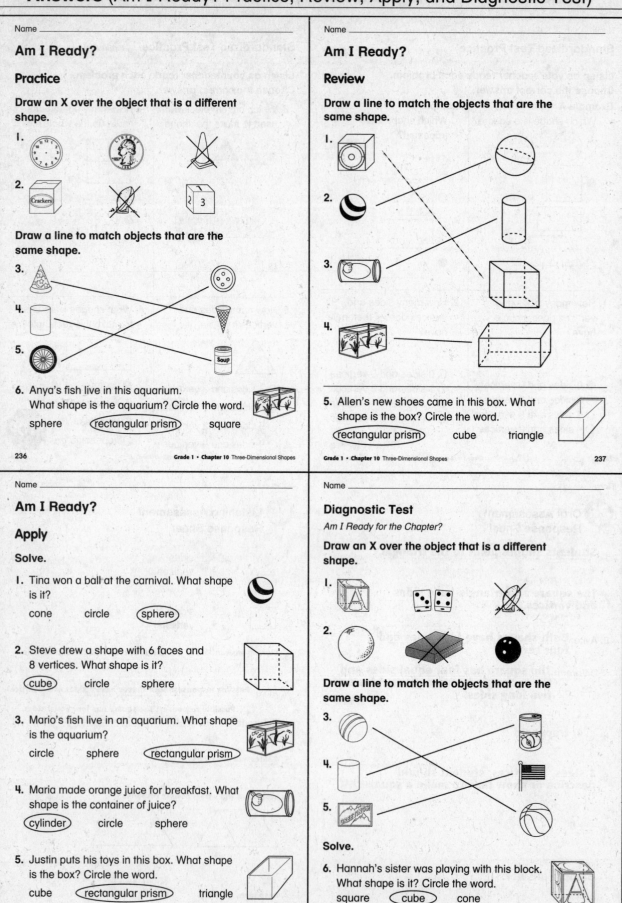

Name _____

Am I Ready?

Practice

Draw an X over the object that is a different shape.

1.

2.

Draw a line to match objects that are the same shape.

3.

4.

5.

6. Anya's fish live in this aquarium. What shape is the aquarium? Circle the word.

sphere   (rectangular prism)   square

236   Grade 1 • **Chapter 10** Three-Dimensional Shapes

Name _____

Am I Ready?

Review

Draw a line to match the objects that are the same shape.

1.

2.

3.

4.

5. Allen's new shoes came in this box. What shape is the box? Circle the word.

(rectangular prism)   cube   triangle

Grade 1 • **Chapter 10** Three-Dimensional Shapes   237

Name _____

Am I Ready?

Apply

Solve.

1. Tina won a ball at the carnival. What shape is it?

   cone   circle   (sphere)

2. Steve drew a shape with 6 faces and 8 vertices. What shape is it?

   (cube)   circle   sphere

3. Mario's fish live in an aquarium. What shape is the aquarium?

   circle   sphere   (rectangular prism)

4. Maria made orange juice for breakfast. What shape is the container of juice?

   (cylinder)   circle   sphere

5. Justin puts his toys in this box. What shape is the box? Circle the word.

   cube   (rectangular prism)   triangle

238   Grade 1 • **Chapter 10** Three-Dimensional Shapes

Name _____

Diagnostic Test

Am I Ready for the Chapter?

Draw an X over the object that is a different shape.

1.

2.

Draw a line to match the objects that are the same shape.

3.

4.

5.

Solve.

6. Hannah's sister was playing with this block. What shape is it? Circle the word.

   square   (cube)   cone

Grade 1 • **Chapter 10** Three-Dimensional Shapes   239

Pretest

Name _____

**Identify each shape. Circle the name.
Write the number of faces and vertices.**

1. cone   (cylinder)

   2 faces **0** vertices

2. cube   rectangular prism

   (cube)

   6 faces **8** vertices

Circle the shapes used to make each composite shape.

3.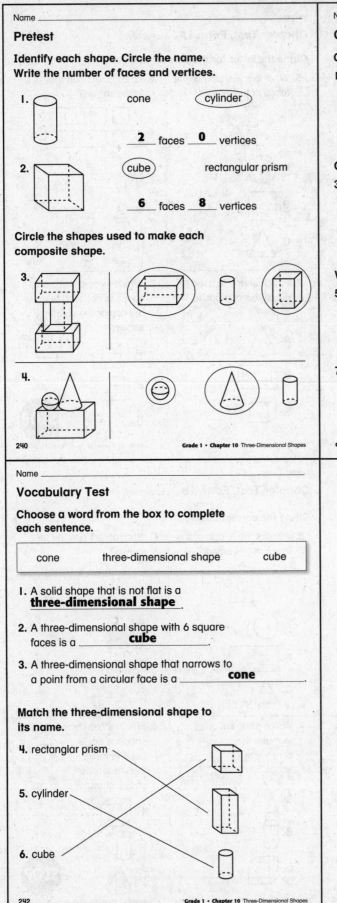

4.

240   **Grade 1 • Chapter 10** Three-Dimensional Shapes

Check My Progress   *(Lessons 1 through 2)*

Name _____

Color all the shapes that match the name.

1. cylinder | 2. cube

Circle the objects that match the description.

3. 6 faces, 8 vertices | 4. 0 faces, 0 vertices

Write how many.

5.   **1** faces
     1 vertices

6.   **6** faces
     8 vertices

7.   **6** faces
     8 vertices

8.   **2** faces
     0 vertices

Grade 1 • Chapter 10 Three-Dimensional Shapes   241

Vocabulary Test

Name _____

Choose a word from the box to complete each sentence.

| cone | three-dimensional shape | cube |

1. A solid shape that is not flat is a
   three-dimensional shape .

2. A three-dimensional shape with 6 square
   faces is a _____ **cube** .

3. A three-dimensional shape that narrows to
   a point from a circular face is a _____ **cone** .

Match the three-dimensional shape to its name.

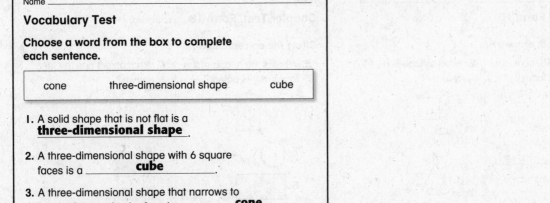

4. rectanglar prism

5. cylinder

6. cube

242   **Grade 1 • Chapter 10** Three-Dimensional Shapes

Answers (Forms IA and IB)

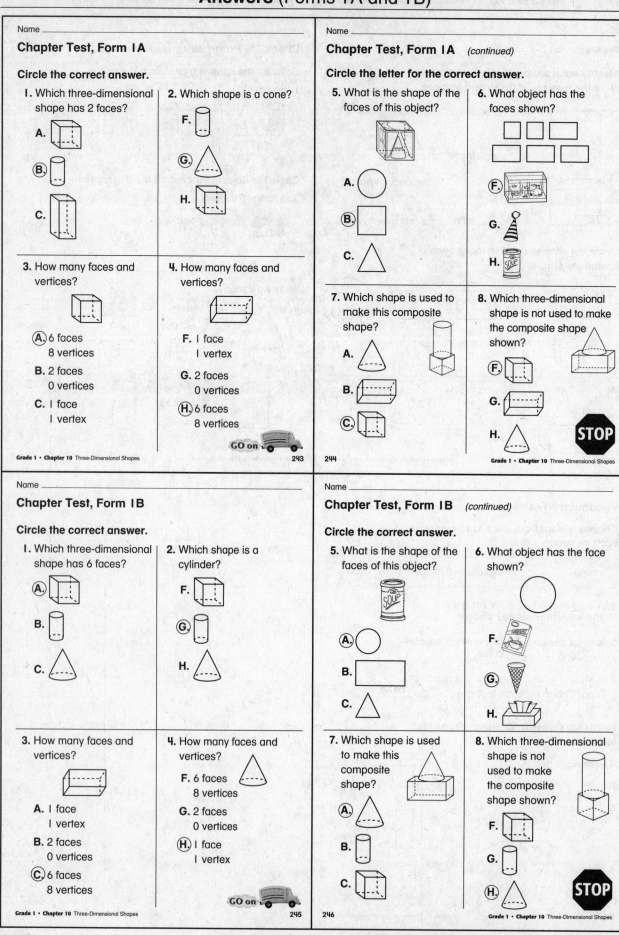

Name _____

Chapter Test, Form IA

Circle the correct answer.

1. Which three-dimensional shape has 2 faces?

A.

(B.)

C.

2. Which shape is a cone?

F.

(G.)

H.

3. How many faces and vertices?

(A.) 6 faces
8 vertices

B. 2 faces
0 vertices

C. I face
I vertex

4. How many faces and vertices?

F. I face
I vertex

G. 2 faces
0 vertices

(H.) 6 faces
8 vertices

GO on

Grade 1 • **Chapter 10** Three-Dimensional Shapes   243

Name _____

Chapter Test, Form IA *(continued)*

Circle the letter for the correct answer.

5. What is the shape of the faces of this object?

A.

(B.)

C.

6. What object has the faces shown?

(F.)

G.

H.

7. Which shape is used to make this composite shape?

A.

B.

(C.)

8. Which three-dimensional shape is not used to make the composite shape shown?

(F.)

G.

H.

STOP

244   Grade 1 • **Chapter 10** Three-Dimensional Shapes

Name _____

Chapter Test, Form IB

Circle the correct answer.

1. Which three-dimensional shape has 6 faces?

(A.)

B.

C.

2. Which shape is a cylinder?

F.

(G.)

H.

3. How many faces and vertices?

A. I face
I vertex

B. 2 faces
0 vertices

(C.) 6 faces
8 vertices

4. How many faces and vertices?

F. 6 faces
8 vertices

G. 2 faces
0 vertices

(H.) I face
I vertex

GO on

Grade 1 • **Chapter 10** Three-Dimensional Shapes   245

Name _____

Chapter Test, Form IB *(continued)*

Circle the correct answer.

5. What is the shape of the faces of this object?

(A.)

B.

C.

6. What object has the face shown?

F.

(G.)

H.

7. Which shape is used to make this composite shape?

(A.)

B.

C.

8. Which three-dimensional shape is not used to make the composite shape shown?

F.

G.

(H.)

STOP

246   Grade 1 • **Chapter 10** Three-Dimensional Shapes

A57

Grade 2 • Chapter 10 Three-Dimensional Shapes

Answers (Forms 2A and 2B)

Name _____

Chapter Test, Form 2A

Circle the correct answer.

1. What is the name of this shape?

   A. cube
   B. cylinder
   C. rectangular prism

2. What is the name of this shape?

   F. cube
   G. cylinder
   H. cone

3. Which shape has 1 face and 1 vertex?

   A.
   B.
   C.

4. Which object has the faces shown?

   F.
   G.
   H.

Name _____

Chapter Test, Form 2A (continued)

Write the correct answer.

5. Circle the name of this three-dimensional shape.

   cube
   rectangular prism

6. Write the number of faces and vertices.

   6 faces
   8 vertices

7. Circle the names of the shapes used to make this composite shape.

   cone
   cylinder
   cube

8. Circle the shape of the faces of this object.

Name _____

Chapter Test, Form 2B

Circle the correct answer.

1. What is the name of this shape?

   A. rectangular prism
   B. cylinder
   C. cube

2. What is the name of this shape?

   F. cone
   G. cube
   H. rectangluar prism

3. Which shape has 2 faces and 0 vertices?

   A.
   B.
   C.

4. Which object has the faces shown?

   F.
   G.
   H.

Name _____

Chapter Test, Form 2B (continued)

Write the correct answer.

5. Circle the name of this three-dimensional shape.

   cylinder
   cube

6. Write the number of faces and vertices.

   1 face
   1 vertex

7. Circle the names of the shapes used to make this composite shape.

   cube
   rectangular prism
   cylinder

8. Circle the shape of the face of this object.

Answers

Answers (Forms 3A and 3B)

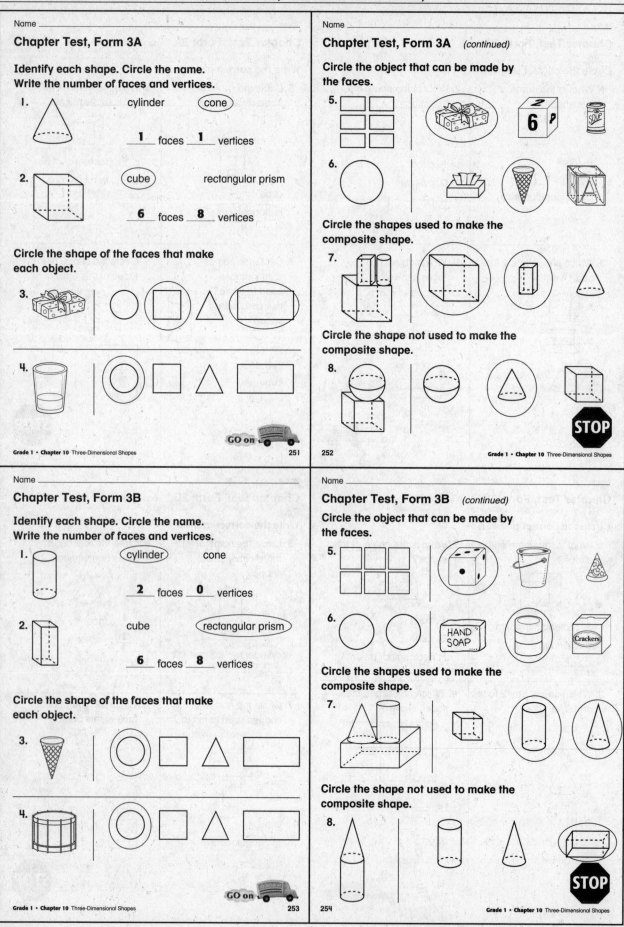

Name _____

Chapter Test, Form 3A

Identify each shape. Circle the name.
Write the number of faces and vertices.

1. cylinder (cone)

     1 faces **1** vertices

2. (cube)   rectangular prism

     6 faces **8** vertices

Circle the shape of the faces that make each object.

3.

4.

GO on

Grade 1 • **Chapter 10** Three-Dimensional Shapes   251

Name _____

Chapter Test, Form 3A *(continued)*

Circle the object that can be made by the faces.

5.

6.

Circle the shapes used to make the composite shape.

7.

Circle the shape not used to make the composite shape.

8.

STOP

252   Grade 1 • **Chapter 10** Three-Dimensional Shapes

Name _____

Chapter Test, Form 3B

Identify each shape. Circle the name.
Write the number of faces and vertices.

1. (cylinder)   cone

     2 faces **0** vertices

2. cube   (rectangular prism)

     6 faces **8** vertices

Circle the shape of the faces that make each object.

3.

4.

GO on

Grade 1 • **Chapter 10** Three-Dimensional Shapes   253

Name _____

Chapter Test, Form 3B *(continued)*

Circle the object that can be made by the faces.

5.

6.

Circle the shapes used to make the composite shape.

7.

Circle the shape not used to make the composite shape.

8.

STOP

254   Grade 1 • **Chapter 10** Three-Dimensional Shapes

A59

Grade 2 • Chapter 10 Three-Dimensional Shapes

Answers (STP, Oral and Listening Assessment Response Sheet)

Name _____

Standardized Test Practice

Listen as your teacher reads each problem.
Choose the correct answer.

Example A

Which three-dimensional shape is a cube?

○ (rectangular prism)
● (cube)
○ (cylinder)
○ (cone)

Example B

Which three-dimensional shape is a cone?

○ (cube)
○ (cylinder)
○ (rectangular prism)
● (cone)

1. How many faces and vertices does a rectangular prism have?

○ 1 face
   1 vertex
○ 2 faces
   0 vertices
○ 3 faces
   1 vertex
● 6 faces
   8 vertices

2. How many faces and vertices does a cone have?

● 1 face
   1 vertex
○ 2 faces
   0 vertices
○ 3 faces
   1 vertex
○ 6 faces
   8 vertices

GO on

Name _____

Standardized Test Practice *(continued)*

3. Which object can be made by the faces shown?

○ (glass)
● (die)
○ (fish tank)
○ (can CARROT)

4. Which shape is used to make the composite shape?

● (cone)
○ (sphere)
○ (cylinder)
○ (rectangular prism)

5. What is the shape of the faces that make up this object? (JUICE)

○ (square)
● (circle)
○ (triangle)
○ (rectangle)

6. Which shape is not used to make the composite shape?

○ (cone)
○ (rectangular prism)
● (sphere)
○ (cylinder)

STOP

Name _____

Oral Assessment Response Sheet

1. **Student should point to the cone. 1 face and 1 vertex**

2. **cylinder; 2 faces, 0 vertices**

3. **6 faces and 8 vertices; Student should draw a square.**

4. **rectangular prism; 6 faces and 8 vertices; 2 squares and 2 rectangles**

5. **Responses will vary. Students should put two or more geometric solids together to create a new shape. They should name the three-dimensional shapes they used to make the new shape.**

Name _____

Listening Assessment Response Sheet

1. **1 face and 1 vertex**

2. **2 faces and 0 vertices**

3. **6 faces and 8 vertices**

4. **6 faces and 8 vertices**

5. **Student should draw 6 squares; square**

6. **Student should draw 2 circles; circle**

7. **Same: Both a cube and a rectangular prism have 6 faces and 8 vertices. Different: 6 squares make up the faces of a cube. A rectangular prism can have 2 squares and 4 rectangles as faces. It can also have 6 rectangles as faces.**

Answers

Name _____

Benchmark Test 1 *(Chapters 1–2)*

Listen as your teacher reads each problem.
Choose the correct answer.

Example A

How many are left?

● 4   ○ 6
○ 7   ○ 8

Example B

How many umbrellas are there in all?

○ 5   ● 7
○ 6   ○ 8

1. Which addition number sentence goes with this picture?

● 4 + 3 = 7
○ 6 + 4 = 10
○ 5 + 4 = 9
○ 6 + 5 = 11

2. Which subtraction sentence goes with this picture?

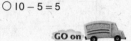

● 8 − 3 = 5
○ 9 − 3 = 6
○ 9 − 4 = 5
○ 10 − 5 = 5

GO on

Grade 1 • Benchmark Tests   261

Name _____

Benchmark Test 1 *(Chapters 1–2)*

Listen as your teacher reads each problem.
Choose the correct answer.

3. 4 + 1 = _____
○ 7
○ 6
● 5
○ 4

4. 2 + 3 = _____
○ 4
● 5
○ 6
○ 7

5. Miles found 3 rocks. He gave 1 to his brother. How many rocks does he have left?
○ 5
○ 4
○ 3
● 2

6. Determine if the statement is true or false.

5 + 3 = 8

● true
○ false

GO on

262   Grade 1 • Benchmark Tests

Name _____

Benchmark Test 1 *(Chapters 1–2)*

Listen as your teacher reads each problem.
Choose the correct answer.

7. Julia had 7 shirts. She gave 3 away. How many shirts does she have left?
○ 5
● 4
○ 3
○ 2

8. 7 − 0 = _____
● 7
○ 6
○ 5
○ 4

9. 5 − 4 = _____
○ 3
○ 2
● 1
○ 0

10. How many hearts are there in all?

○ 3
○ 6
○ 5
● 7

STOP

Grade 1 • Benchmark Tests   263

Grade 1 • Benchmark Tests

Answers (Benchmark Test 2)

Name _____

Benchmark Test 2 *(Chapters 3–4)*

Listen as your teacher reads each problem.
Choose the correct answer.

Example A

Use the number line to subtract. What is the difference?

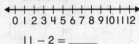
0 1 2 3 4 5 6 7 8 9 10 11 12

11 − 2 = _____

○ 7　　○ 8
● 9　　○ 10

Example B

Start with the greater number. Count on to add.

4 + 2 = _____

○ 4　　○ 5
● 6　　○ 7

1. Rose had 5 pennies. She got 2 more. How many pennies does Rose have now?

○ 4　　○ 5
○ 6　　● 7

2. Which subtraction number sentence goes with the story?

Kris sees 7 fish. 6 fish swim away. How many fish are left?

○ 7 − 3 = 4
● 7 − 6 = 1
○ 7 − 5 = 2
○ 6 + 1 = 7

GO on

264   **Grade 1 · Benchmark Tests**

Name _____

Benchmark Test 2 *(Chapters 3–4)*

Listen as your teacher reads each problem.
Choose the correct answer.

3. Add the doubles. Add the other number to find the sum.

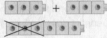 + 3 = **15**

● 15　　○ 13
○ 11　　○ 9

4. The puppy slept for 2 hours in the morning. He slept 2 hours after a walk and 1 hour before dinner. How many hours did the puppy sleep altogether?

○ 2　　● 5
○ 4　　○ 6

5. What is the related subtraction fact?

5 + 2 = 7

○ 9 − 7 = 2
○ 9 − 5 = 4
○ 5 − 2 = 3
● 7 − 5 = 2

6. Add the doubles fact. Then subtract. Which number shows the difference?

3 + 3 = 6

6 − 3 = _____

○ 4　　● 3
○ 2　　○ 1

GO on

Grade 1 · Benchmark Tests   265

Name _____

Benchmark Test 2 *(Chapters 3–4)*

Listen as your teacher reads each problem.
Choose the correct answer.

7. Which number sentence shows a missing addend?

○ 3 + 7 = ☐

● ☐ + 7 = 10

8. Use the number line to add. Write the sum.

0 1 2 3 4 5 6 7 8 9 10 11 12

7 + 2 = _____

○ 7
○ 8
● 9
○ 10

9. Which subtraction number sentence is part of this fact family?

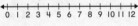

4 + 5 = 9
5 + 4 = 9
9 − 5 = 4

○ 9 − 3 = 6
○ 9 + 5 = 14
● 9 − 4 = 5
○ 9 − 2 = 7

10.
1 2 3 4 5 6 7 8 9 10

Use the number line to subtract.

8 − 3 = _____

○ 7
○ 6
● 5
○ 4

266   **Grade 1 · Benchmark Tests**

Grade 1 · Benchmark Tests   **A62**

Answers

Answers (Benchmark Test 3)

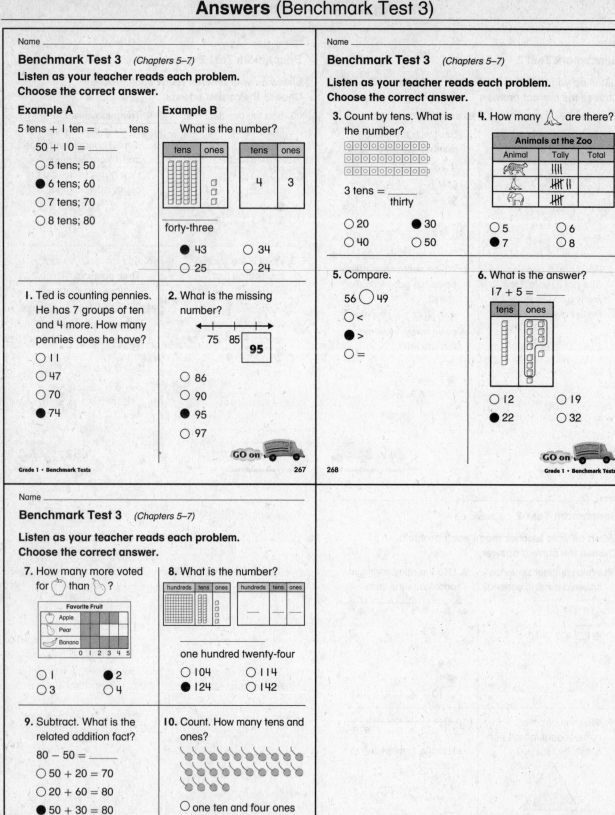

Name _____

Benchmark Test 3 *(Chapters 5–7)*

Listen as your teacher reads each problem.
Choose the correct answer.

Example A

5 tens + 1 ten = _____ tens

50 + 10 = _____

○ 5 tens; 50
● 6 tens; 60
○ 7 tens; 70
○ 8 tens; 80

Example B

What is the number?

tens	ones

tens	ones
4	3

forty-three

● 43   ○ 34
○ 25   ○ 24

1. Ted is counting pennies. He has 7 groups of ten and 4 more. How many pennies does he have?

○ 11
○ 47
○ 70
● 74

2. What is the missing number?

75 85 **95**

○ 86
○ 90
● 95
○ 97

GO on

Grade 1 • Benchmark Tests   267

Name _____

Benchmark Test 3 *(Chapters 5–7)*

Listen as your teacher reads each problem.
Choose the correct answer.

3. Count by tens. What is the number?

3 tens = _____
thirty

○ 20   ● 30
○ 40   ○ 50

4. How many 🦅 are there?

Animals at the Zoo		
Animal	Tally	Total
	IIII	
	ЖЖ II	
	ЖЖ	

○ 5   ○ 6
● 7   ○ 8

5. Compare.

56 ○ 49

○ <
● >
○ =

6. What is the answer?

17 + 5 = _____

tens	ones

○ 12   ○ 19
● 22   ○ 32

GO on

Grade 1 • Benchmark Tests

268

Name _____

Benchmark Test 3 *(Chapters 5–7)*

Listen as your teacher reads each problem.
Choose the correct answer.

7. How many more voted for 🍎 than 🍐?

Favorite Fruit

Apple					
Pear					
Banana					
0 1 2 3 4 5

○ 1   ● 2
○ 3   ○ 4

8. What is the number?

hundreds	tens	ones

hundreds	tens	ones
—	—	—

one hundred twenty-four

○ 104   ○ 114
● 124   ○ 142

9. Subtract. What is the related addition fact?

80 − 50 = _____

○ 50 + 20 = 70
○ 20 + 60 = 80
● 50 + 30 = 80
○ 50 + 40 = 90

10. Count. How many tens and ones?

○ one ten and four ones
○ one ten and fourteen ones
● two tens and four ones
○ twenty-four ones

STOP

Grade 1 • Benchmark Tests   269

A63

Grade 1 • Benchmark Tests

Answers (Benchmark Test 4)

Name _____

Benchmark Test 4 (Chapters 1–10)

**Listen as your teacher reads each question.
Choose the correct answer.**

Example A

How many birds in all?

○3 ○5 ●6 ○8

Example B

Count back to subtract.
Start with 5.

5 − 2 = _____

●3 ○2 ○1 ○0

1. How many stars are there in all?

○3 ○6 ○5 ●7

2. Count on to add.

4 + 3 = _____

○4
○5
○6
●7

3. Count by tens. What is the number?

2 tens = _____
             twenty

●20   ○40
○60   ○80

270

Name _____

Benchmark Test 4 (Chapters 1–10)

4. Subtract.

6 tens − 2 tens = _____ tens

60 − 20 = _____

○ 3 tens; 30
● 4 tens, 40
○ 5 tens, 50
○ 6 tens, 60

5. How many 🐘 are there?

Animals at the Zoo		
Animal	Tally	Total
🐯	IIII	
🦅	HHT II	
🐘	HHT	

●5 ○6 ○7 ○8

6. Which ribbon is the shortest?

○
●
○

7. How many sides and vertices does a circle have?

● 0 sides and 0 vertices
○ 3 sides and 3 vertices
○ 4 sides and 4 vertices
○ 4 sides and 2 vertices

8. Which object can be made by the faces below?

9. What time is it?

○ 10 o'clock
● half past 10
○ 11 o'clock
○ half past 11

271

Name _____

Benchmark Test 4 (Chapters 1–10)

10. Which pattern block was used to make the shape.

11. What is the shape of the faces that make up the object?

JUICE

○ □ ● ○
○ △
○ ▭

12. Which shape is not used to make the composite shape?

13. Choose the rectangle that has a quarter of its shape shaded.

14. Subtract.

5 − 4 = _____

○3 ○2 ●1 ○0

15. Add.

5 + 6 = _____

●11 ○10 ○9 ○8

272

Name _____

Benchmark Test 4 (Chapters 1–10)

16. What is the related subtraction fact?

7 + 7 = 14

● 14 − 7 = 7
○ 15 − 9 = 6
○ 16 − 8 = 8
○ 17 − 9 = 6

17. Count from 29 to 35. What number comes next?

1	2	3	4	5	6	7	8	9	10
11	12	13	14	15	16	17	18	19	20
21	22	23	24	25	26	27	28	29	30
31	32	33	34	35	36	37	38	39	40

● 36   ○ 29
○ 38   ○ 19

18. Subtract.

9 tens − 2 tens = _____ tens

90 − 20 = _____

● 7 tens, 70
○ 5 tens, 50
○ 2 tens, 20
○ 1 tens, 10

19. Look at the tally chart. How many more people voted for the ○ than the ★?

Favorite Shape		
Shape	Tally	Total
○ Circle	HHT II	
★ Star	HHT	
△ Triangle	HHT I	

● 2 ○ 3 ○ 4 ○ 5

20. Which fish is the longest?

○
●
○

273

Answers

Answers (Benchmark Test 4)

Benchmark Test 4 *(Chapters 1–10)*

21. How many sides and vertices does a rectangle have?

○ 0 sides and 0 vertices
○ 3 sides and 3 vertices
● 4 sides and 4 vertices
○ 4 sides and 0 vertices

22. Which shape is used to make the composite shape?

● △ ○ ⬤
○ ▯ ○ ▱

23. Count by fives. How much in all?

○ 30¢
● 25¢
○ 20¢
○ 15¢

24. Add the doubles. Add the other number to find the sum.

⑤ + ⑤ + 3 = _____

[**10**]

○ 15
● 13
○ 11
○ 9

GO on

274

Grade 1 • Benchmark Tests

Benchmark Test 4 *(Chapters 1–10)*

25. What time is it?

9:30

● half past 9
○ 9 o'clock
○ half past 8

26. What time is it?

○ 6 o'clock
● 7 o'clock
○ half past 7

27. Which shape is a square?

○ ○
● ▢
○ ▭
○ ⬯

28. Which three-dimensional shape is the cube?

○ ▱
● ⬛
○ ▯
○ △

29. Subtract. What is the related addition fact?

80 − 50 = _____

○ 50 + 20 = 70
○ 20 + 60 = 80
● 50 + 30 = 80
○ 50 + 40 = 90

30. About how many cubes long is the pencil?

○ about 7 cubes
● about 8 cubes
○ about 9 cubes

STOP

Grade 1 • Benchmark Tests

275

A65

Grade 1 • Benchmark Tests